GAME PAD

celador
international

ISBN-13: 9-781-84239-641-4
ISBN-10: 1-84239-641-2

© 2006 Celador International Ltd
Published in 2006 by
ALLIGATOR BOOKS LIMITED
Gadd House, Arcadia Avenue, London N3 2JU
Printed in Malaysia

GAME 1

1) £100
Which of these is an offensive weapon?
- A: Thumb polisher
- B: Wrist wiper
- C: Knuckle duster
- D: Nail cleaner

2) £200
Whose 'World' was the subject of a 1992 comedy film starring Mike Myers?
- A: Paul's
- B: Jeff's
- C: Tony's
- D: Wayne's

3) £300
Complete the famous quote from 'The Godfather', 'I'll make him... he can't refuse.'
- A: An offer
- B: A pizza
- C: A suggestion
- D: A jacket

4) £500
What did Tom Hanks play in the 2000 film 'Cast Away'?
- A: Crash survivor
- B: Sculptor
- C: Dustman
- D: Fly fisherman

5) £1,000
Complete the famous line by the poet William Wordsworth, 'I wandered lonely a ...'?
- A: Leaf
- B: Feather
- C: Cloud
- D: Bird

You have won at least £1,000!

6) £2,000
Which of these is the title of a Martin Scorsese film starring Robert De Niro and Sharon Stone?
- A: Tombola
- B: Casino
- C: Concerto
- D: Bingo

7) £4,000
Which character is played by Mel Gibson in the 'Lethal Weapon' series of films?
- A: Johnny Briggs
- B: Billy Spriggs
- C: Martin Riggs
- D: Ryan Giggs

8) £8,000
Omar Sharif played the title role in which of these films?
- A: Ben-Hur
- B: Doctor Zhivago
- C: The Godfather
- D: Becket

9) £16,000
For which film did Elton John compose his Oscar-winning song 'Can you feel the love tonight?'?
- A: Pocahontas
- B: The Lion King
- C: Aladdin
- D: Finding Nemo

10) £32,000
Whose autobiography is entitled 'Jolly Green Giant'?
- A: Terry Nutkins
- B: David Bellamy
- C: David Prowse
- D: Lou Ferrigno

You have won at least £32,000!

11) £64,000
Which was John Wayne's last film?
- A: True Grit
- B: McQ
- C: The Shootist
- D: Brannigan

12) £125,000
Which actress co-founded a film production company called Simian Films?
- A: Minnie Driver
- B: Kate Winslet
- C: Liz Hurley
- D: Julie Walters

13) £250,000
Who was the first British golfer to win the US Masters?
- A: Tony Jacklin
- B: Nick Faldo
- C: Sandy Lyle
- D: Ian Woosnam

14) £500,000
In which city was the explorer John Cabot born?
- A: Cadiz
- B: Bristol
- C: Lisbon
- D: Genoa

15) £1,000,000
Who are the most feared inhabitants of the planet Skaro?
- A: The Cylons
- B: The Triffids
- C: The Borg
- D: The Daleks

CONGRATULATIONS YOU ARE A MILLIONAIRE!

GAME 1 ANSWERS PAGE 60

50:50 from page 52

Ask The Audience from page 56

Phone-A-Friend

GAME 2

1) £100
Which of these words means nonsense?
- A: Pilchardsclout
- B: Codswallop
- C: Troutsthump
- D: Sardinesbash

2) £200
What nationality is the former film star Brigitte Bardot?
- A: English
- B: French
- C: Chinese
- D: Welsh

3) £300
Which of these cartoon characters has a girlfriend called Daisy?
- A: Mickey Mouse
- B: Donald Duck
- C: Jiminy Cricket
- D: Dumbo

4) £500
Which of these was a hit single for the pop group Aqua?
- A: Action Man
- B: Barbie Girl
- C: Sindy Doll
- D: Game Boy

5) £1,000
Which annual British arts prize was named after an artist?
- A: Goya
- B: Turner
- C: Stubbs
- D: Gainsborough

You have won at least £1,000!

6) £2,000
Which band released the album 'The Wall?'
- A: Black Sabbath
- B: Pink Floyd
- C: Green Day
- D: Orange Juice

7) £4,000
Tintin's nautical companion is Captain ...?
- A: Pugwash
- B: Bass
- C: Barnacle
- D: Haddock

8) £8,000
Kerry McFadden is a former member of which pop group?
- A: Bananarama
- B: Catatonia
- C: Atomic Kitten
- D: Texas

9) £16,000
Which TV chef is married to the presenter Fern Britton?
- A: James Martin
- B: Gary Rhodes
- C: Jamie Oliver
- D: Phil Vickery

10) £32,000
Which fictional football team is central to the plot of the ITV series 'Footballers' Wives'?
- A: Barons Albion
- B: Earls Park
- C: Kings Villa
- D: Dukes Argyle

You have won at least £32,000!

11) £64,000
Who said of her Oscar, 'I feel for 8 minutes on screen I should only get a little bit of him'?
- A: Julia Roberts
- B: Judi Dench
- C: Helen Hunt
- D: Nicole Kidman

12) £125,000
Who wrote the children's book 'Charlotte's Web'?
- A: Nina Bawden
- B: E Nesbit
- C: Roald Dahl
- D: E B White

13) £250,000
Who was the first European to cross the Pacific Ocean?
- A: Drake
- B: Cabot
- C: Magellan
- D: Columbus

14) £500,000
In European mythology, which is the archaic term for a supernatural being?
- A: Blak
- B: Blew
- C: Wight
- D: Gray

15) £1,000,000
What is Jude Law's first forename?
- A: Donald
- B: Derek
- C: David
- D: Duncan

GAME 2 ANSWERS PAGE 60

50:50 from page 52
Ask The Audience from page 56
Phone-A-Friend

CONGRATULATIONS YOU ARE A MILLIONAIRE!

3

GAME 3

1) £100

At what type of office is a wedding most likely to take place?

A: Tax
B: Register
C: Betting
D: Post

2) £200

Which television family have broadcasted a weekly comedy chat show from its house at No 42?

A: The Osbournes
B: The Cosbys
C: The Kumars
D: The Blairs

3) £300

In film and TV, what is a head-and-shoulders shot of an actor called?

A: Mug shot
B: Blow up
C: Close-up
D: Take

4) £500

Which name is synonymous with the University of Paris?

A: Sorbitol
B: Sorbet
C: Sorbonne
D: Sorbose

5) £1,000

Which county is associated with a breed of bull terrier?

A: Derbyshire
B: Leicestershire
C: Staffordshire
D: Oxfordshire

You have won at least £1,000!

6) £2,000

Who played Clarice Starling in the 1991 film 'The Silence of the Lambs'?

A: Sandra Bullock
B: Julia Roberts
C: Jodie Foster
D: Demi Moore

7) £4,000

Which rock star married the model Iman in 1992?

A: David Bowie
B: Meat Loaf
C: Jon Bon Jovi
D: Eric Clapton

8) £8,000

Where does the Fastnet yacht race begin?

A: Land's End
B: Cowes
C: Great Yarmouth
D: Hull

9) £16,000

Which of these is a traditional ingredient of Scotch broth?

A: Porridge oats
B: Rice
C: Pearl barley
D: Rye

10) £32,000

Which Shakespeare play features a character called Sir Toby Belch?

A: The Tempest
B: Henry V
C: Twelfth Night
D: As You Like It

You have won at least £32,000!

11) £64,000

Who was the US president at the outbreak of World War I?

A: Harry S Truman
B: Herbert Hoover
C: William Taft
D: Woodrow Wilson

12) £125,000

Who wrote the poem which begins 'Do not go gentle into that good night'?

A: Wilfred Owen
B: Ted Hughes
C: W B Yeats
D: Dylan Thomas

13) £250,000

Who married Roy Rogers in 1947?

A: Veronica Lake
B: Betty Grable
C: Betty Hutton
D: Dale Evans

14) £500,000

Which comedian hangs from a clockface in the 1923 silent film 'Safety Last'?

A: Buster Keaton
B: Will Hay
C: Harry Langdon
D: Harold Lloyd

15) £1,000,000

Which dramatist acted in provincial theatre under the name of David Baron?

A: Samuel Beckett
B: Harold Pinter
C: Noël Coward
D: John Osborne

GAME 3 ANSWERS PAGE 60

50:50 from page 52
Ask The Audience from page 56
Phone-A-Friend

CONGRATULATIONS YOU ARE A MILLIONAIRE!

4

GAME 4

1) £100
Complete the name of the vegetable, ... sprout?
- A: Paris
- B: Hague
- C: Brussels
- D: Rotterdam

2) £200
Which of these creatures are sometimes used to carry messages?
- A: Rats
- B: Pigeons
- C: Lions
- D: Goldfish

3) £300
Which of these is a Spanish national dance?
- A: Bolero
- B: Mosquito
- C: Tornado
- D: Bingo

4) £500
Which of these is not a toy or miniature breed of dog?
- A: Chihuahua
- B: Pug
- C: Pekingese
- D: Dalmatian

5) £1,000
Which of these is a breed of spaniel?
- A: Prince Harry
- B: Prince William
- C: King Charles
- D: Lady Helen

You have won at least £1,000!

6) £2,000
Wayne Rooney signed for which football club in 2004?
- A: Liverpool
- B: Everton
- C: Manchester United
- D: Leeds United

7) £4,000
In which country is the island of Java?
- A: India
- B: Thailand
- C: Indonesia
- D: Malaysia

8) £8,000
Which city is the state capital of Texas?
- A: Dallas
- B: Austin
- C: Houston
- D: San Antonio

9) £16,000
What is the family name of the ruling house of Monaco?
- A: Berlusconi
- B: Grimaldi
- C: Rothschild
- D: Bourbon

10) £32,000
Deborah Messing stars in which US sitcom?
- A: Friends
- B: Suddenly Susan
- C: Will and Grace
- D: Frasier

You have won at least £32,000!

11) £64,000
The Formula 1 Grand Prix season traditionally starts in which country?
- A: France
- B: Italy
- C: Spain
- D: Australia

12) £125,000
Which of the following is not a famous footballer?
- A: Diogenes
- B: Leonidas
- C: Carecas
- D: Socrates

13) £250,000
In the sitcom 'Frasier', what is the name of Martin Crane's dog?
- A: Jimmy
- B: Freddie
- C: Eddie
- D: Sammy

14) £500,000
Which of these is a central character in Jane Austen's novel 'Persuasion'?
- A: Arabella Allen
- B: Nancy Lammeter
- C: Becky Sharp
- D: Anne Elliot

15) £1,000,000
The siege of which town was the last major battle of the American Revolution?
- A: Yorktown
- B: Boston
- C: Lexington
- D: Hartford

GAME 4 ANSWERS PAGE 60

50:50 from page 52
Ask The Audience from page 56
Phone-A-Friend

CONGRATULATIONS YOU ARE A MILLIONAIRE!

GAME 5

1) £100
Paul Hogan's most famous film character is 'Crocodile ...'?
- A: Glasgow
- B: Dundee
- C: Edinburgh
- D: Aberdeen

2) £200
Which animal is sometimes referred to as the 'ship of the desert'?
- A: Elephant
- B: Camel
- C: Cow
- D: Rhinoceros

3) £300
In which country is the Taj Mahal?
- A: India
- B: Russia
- C: Japan
- D: Saudi Arabia

4) £500
What is the main diet of the elephant?
- A: Insects
- B: Fish
- C: Plants
- D: Small mammals

5) £1,000
Which creatures produce royal jelly?
- A: Spiders
- B: Beetles
- C: Caterpillars
- D: Bees

You have won at least £1,000!

6) £2,000
In the TV sitcom, what are the friends in 'Friends'?
- A: Philadelphians
- B: Washingtonians
- C: New Yorkers
- D: Bostonians

7) £4,000
In which English county is Scafell Pike?
- A: Cumbria
- B: Derbyshire
- C: Durham
- D: Shropshire

8) £8,000
The TV soap 'Neighbours' is set in a fictional suburb of which city?
- A: Sydney
- B: Perth
- C: Adelaide
- D: Melbourne

9) £16,000
As of 2004, who was the last British actress to win a Best Actress Oscar?
- A: Judi Dench
- B: Maggie Smith
- C: Emma Thompson
- D: Glenda Jackson

10) £32,000
Football's Euro 2008 will be co-hosted by Austria and which other country?
- A: Switzerland
- B: Germany
- C: Slovakia
- D: Liechtenstein

You have won at least £32,000!

11) £64,000
Who renamed Dorchester as Casterbridge in their novel?
- A: Thomas Hardy
- B: Jane Austin
- C: George Eliot
- D: Henry Fielding

12) £125,000
'Vile Bodies' is a novel by which author?
- A: Graham Greene
- B: Aldous Huxley
- C: Evelyn Waugh
- D: Kingsley Amis

13) £250,000
In TV's 'Star Trek: The Next Generation', who has a positronic brain?
- A: Guinan
- B: Data
- C: Troi
- D: La Forge

14) £500,000
In March 2003, which horse became the first in 32 years to retain the Cheltenham Gold Cup?
- A: Sir Rembrandt
- B: Best Mate
- C: Harbour Pilot
- D: Valley Henry

15) £1,000,000
Which of these was the Greek god of earthquakes?
- A: Hephaestos
- B: Kronos
- C: Poseidon
- D: Ares

CONGRATULATIONS YOU ARE A MILLIONAIRE!

GAME 5 ANSWERS PAGE 60

50:50 from page 52
Ask The Audience from page 56
Phone-A-Friend

6

GAME 6

1) £100
Complete the title of this 1989 film, 'Honey, I Shrunk ...'?
- A: The Kids
- B: The Cat
- C: The Jeans
- D: The Budget

2) £200
A bullock is a young male what?
- A: Deer
- B: Pig
- C: Steer
- D: Dog

3) £300
Which is the capital city of the USA?
- A: Washington DC
- B: New York
- C: Los Angeles
- D: Chicago

4) £500
What is the collective term for a country's passenger and cargo ships?
- A: Retailer navy
- B: Merchant navy
- C: Trader navy
- D: Salesman navy

5) £1,000
Kleptomania is a compulsive urge to do what?
- A: Start fires
- B: Eat
- C: Lie
- D: Steal

You have won at least £1,000!

6) £2,000
On a musical score, what does 'presto' mean?
- A: Quick
- B: Loud
- C: Strong
- D: Very slow

7) £4,000
Queen Nefertiti was once the ruler of which country?
- A: India
- B: Greece
- C: Persia
- D: Egypt

8) £8,000
Who played the title role in the 1998 film 'Elizabeth'?
- A: Judi Dench
- B: Cate Blanchett
- C: Hilary Swank
- D: Nicole Kidman

9) £16,000
Which of these novels opens with the line, 'Last night I dreamt I went to Manderley again'?
- A: Jane Eyre
- B: Rebecca
- C: Emma
- D: Heidi

10) £32,000
To susurrate means to do what?
- A: Chat
- B: Shout
- C: Swear
- D: Whisper

You have won at least £32,000!

11) £64,000
The Great Fire of London occurred during the reign of which monarch?
- A: Elizabeth I
- B: Charles II
- C: Anne
- D: George IV

12) £125,000
Gadshill, near Rochester in Kent, was the home of which writer?
- A: Dickens
- B: H G Wells
- C: Virginia Woolf
- D: D H Lawrence

13) £250,000
Which is Iceland's most famous volcano?
- A: Kilauea
- B: Hekla
- C: Erebus
- D: Taal

14) £500,000
What kind of ladies' accessory was a reticule?
- A: Bag
- B: Sash
- C: Hatpin
- D: Parasol

15) £1,000,000
To which island is the nocturnal primate called the aye-aye native?
- A: Madagascar
- B: Tasmania
- C: Sri Lanka
- D: Mauritius

CONGRATULATIONS YOU ARE A MILLIONAIRE!

GAME 6 ANSWERS PAGE 60

50:50 from page 52

Ask The Audience from page 56

Phone-A-Friend

7

GAME 7

1) £100
Which of these is a shout of disapproval sometimes heard from members of an audience?
- A: Catcall
- B: Dogyell
- C: Rabbitshout
- D: Hamstersqueal

2) £200
What are the usual colours of a ladybird?
- A: Green & pink
- B: Red & black
- C: Silver & brown
- D: Blue & white

3) £300
Which word would greet you on arrival in Hawaii?
- A: Aloha
- B: Alumnus
- C: Alamo
- D: Alfalfa

4) £500
Which of these is a major British sportswear retailer?
- A: BBC
- B: VIP
- C: JJB
- D: QED

5) £1,000
Complete the name of the famous London department store, Harvey ...?
- A: Rogers
- B: Nichols
- C: Peters
- D: Williams

You have won at least £1,000!

6) £2,000
The TV series 'Blackadder Goes Forth' was set in which war?
- A: WWI
- B: Boer War
- C: 100 Years' War
- D: WWII

7) £4,000
Which fishy blockbuster was based on a novel by Peter Benchley?
- A: Finding Nemo
- B: Jaws
- C: Piranha
- D: Moby Dick

8) £8,000
Which popular variety of tea is flavoured with bergamot?
- A: Oolong
- B: Earl Grey
- C: Gunpowder
- D: Darjeeling

9) £16,000
Which acid takes its name from the Latin word meaning 'leaf'?
- A: Tannic
- B: Folic
- C: Acetic
- D: Nitric

10) £32,000
What fraction of an academic year is a semester?
- A: Quarter
- B: Half
- C: Third
- D: Eighth

You have won at least £32,000!

11) £64,000
In Beatrix Potter's stories, what kind of animal is Mr Tod?
- A: Rabbit
- B: Squirrel
- C: Fox
- D: Pig

12) £125,000
The wine Tokay originated in which country?
- A: Germany
- B: Hungary
- C: Japan
- D: Bulgaria

13) £250,000
What were the poet T S Eliot's forenames?
- A: Terence Stuart
- B: Thadeus Soames
- C: Trevor Saliens
- D: Thomas Stearns

14) £500,000
In the book 'The Lion, the Witch and the Wardrobe', what type of creature is Mr Tumnus?
- A: Beaver
- B: Faun
- C: Lion
- D: Fox

15) £1,000,000
The park called the Plains of Abraham lies within which Canadian city's limits?
- A: Vancouver
- B: Montreal
- C: Toronto
- D: Quebec

CONGRATULATIONS YOU ARE A MILLIONAIRE!

GAME 7 ANSWERS PAGE 60

50:50 from page 52

Ask The Audience from page 56

Phone-A-Friend

8

GAME 8

1) £100
Which of these is the name given to the room in a house for general family use?
- A: Breathing room
- B: Being room
- C: Living room
- D: Existing room

2) £200
What do giant pandas mainly eat?
- A: Bamboo shoots
- B: Doughnuts
- C: Hamburgers
- D: Pizza

3) £300
'City of Angels' is an informal name for which US city?
- A: Philadelphia
- B: Pennsylvania
- C: Los Angeles
- D: Salt Lake City

4) £500
'Thou' is an old-fashioned way of saying what?
- A: You
- B: He
- C: They
- D: We

5) £1,000
What word is used in the USA for petrol?
- A: Kerosene
- B: Derv
- C: Gasoline
- D: Butane

You have won at least £1,000!

6) £2,000
Which song has been a UK No 1 single for both the Bangles and Atomic Kitten?
- A: Manic Monday
- B: Right Now
- C: See Ya
- D: Eternal Flame

7) £4,000
Paul Whitehouse and Charlie Higson played characters on which TV show?
- A: The Office
- B: The Fast Show
- C: My Family
- D: Father Ted

8) £8,000
Who was the last US president to die in office?
- A: F D Roosevelt
- B: L B Johnson
- C: Harry Truman
- D: John Kennedy

9) £16,000
Freddie Eynsford-Hill is a character in which musical?
- A: Salad Days
- B: My Fair Lady
- C: Me and My Girl
- D: Kiss Me Kate

10) £32,000
In which country did Charlie Chaplin die?
- A: Scotland
- B: Sweden
- C: Switzerland
- D: Spain

You have won at least £32,000!

11) £64,000
Kandahar is the former capital of which country?
- A: Afghanistan
- B: Vietnam
- C: Ukraine
- D: Pakistan

12) £125,000
Which English king had the sobriquet 'Rufus'?
- A: Henry II
- B: William II
- C: Edward II
- D: Harold II

13) £250,000
What colour is the middle stripe of the national flag of The Netherlands?
- A: Red
- B: White
- C: Blue
- D: Orange

14) £500,000
Which country do the pop trio Lasgo come from?
- A: Belgium
- B: France
- C: Italy
- D: Sweden

15) £1,000,000
Which king was given the nickname 'The English Justinian'
- A: Henry VIII
- B: William I
- C: Edward I
- D: Charles II

CONGRATULATIONS YOU ARE A MILLIONAIRE!

GAME 8 ANSWERS PAGE 60

50:50 from page 52
Ask The Audience from page 56
Phone-A-Friend

GAME 9

1) £100
Which of these is the act or ceremony of crowning a monarch?
- A: Carnation
- B: Correlation
- C: Coronation
- D: Constellation

2) £200
Which of these can be attached to the muzzle of a fireman?
- A: Baronet
- B: Bayonet
- C: Baritone
- D: Balaclava

3) £300
Portugal shares a land border with which country?
- A: Morocco
- B: France
- C: Italy
- D: Spain

4) £500
In the phrase 'con trick', 'con' is short for which word?
- A: Continuation
- B: Confidence
- C: Conceit
- D: Concoction

5) £1,000
'Follically-challenged' is a polite way of describing someone as what?
- A: Overweight
- B: Bald
- C: Short
- D: Stupid

You have won at least £1,000!

6) £2,000
Who, aged 58, played the father of a 46-year-old Harrison Ford in an 'Indiana Jones' film?
- A: Peter O'Toole
- B: Sean Connery
- C: Paul Newman
- D: Jack Lemmon

7) £4,000
Which Shakespeare play opens with a shipwreck?
- A: Henry V
- B: Hamlet
- C: King Lear
- D: The Tempest

8) £8,000
In which Canadian province is French the only official language?
- A: Ontario
- B: Quebec
- C: Alberta
- D: Manitoba

9) £16,000
In which TV series did Robin Williams make his name?
- A: Bewitched
- B: Mork and Mindy
- C: Taxi
- D: Mister Ed

10) £32,000
What type of food is Swiss raclette?
- A: Chocolate
- B: Cheese
- C: Potato cake
- D: Smoked sausage

You have won at least £32,000!

11) £64,000
Who won the Men's 800 metres gold medal at the 1980 Olympic Games?
- A: Sebastian Coe
- B: Steve Cram
- C: Peter Elliott
- D: Steve Ovett

12) £125,000
Which city is the capital of the Lazio region of Italy?
- A: Milan
- B: Florence
- C: Naples
- D: Rome

13) £250,000
What stroke is used first in a relay medley swimming race?
- A: Butterfly
- B: Breaststroke
- C: Backstroke
- D: Freestyle

14) £500,000
Elaine Benes is a character in which US sitcom?
- A: Friends
- B: Seinfeld
- C: Roseanne
- D: Spin City

15) £1,000,000
Which was not one of the forenames of the author of 'Murder on the Orient Express'?
- A: Agatha
- B: Jennifer
- C: Mary
- D: Clarissa

GAME 9 ANSWERS PAGE 60

50:50 from page 52

Ask The Audience from page 56

Phone-A-Friend

CONGRATULATIONS YOU ARE A MILLIONAIRE!

GAME 10

1) £100
Which of these is a piece of open land, often at the centre of a hamlet or community?
- A: Village red
- B: Village green
- C: Village blue
- D: Village yellow

2) £200
In which type of painting are you most likely to see boats and ships?
- A: Skyscape
- B: Landscape
- C: Seascape
- D: Cloudscape

3) £300
Which of these is a Caribbean island?
- A: Rockall
- B: Barbados
- C: Sicily
- D: Crete

4) £500
Which type of music is so called because it was originally performed in a room?
- A: Boudoir music
- B: Bathroom music
- C: Study music
- D: Chamber music

5) £1,000
The popular stage show 'Riverdance' is based on traditional dancing from which country?
- A: Ireland
- B: Thailand
- C: Russia
- D: Japan

You have won at least £1,000!

6) £2,000
In 2003, Arnold Schwarzenegger was elected governor of which US state?
- A: Arizona
- B: California
- C: Idaho
- D: Wisconsin

7) £4,000
Which London square features in the chorus of the wartime song 'It's A Long Way To Tipperary'?
- A: Soho
- B: Trafalgar
- C: Leicester
- D: Berkeley

8) £8,000
Which of the following did Tom Hanks play in the 1999 film 'The Green Mile'?
- A: Prison Officer
- B: Athlete
- C: Gardener
- D: Painter

9) £16,000
Which of these London landmarks is in Whitehall?
- A: Eros
- B: Traitor's Gate
- C: Aldgate Pump
- D: The Cenotaph

10) £32,000
Which of these Pankhursts was the mother of the other three?
- A: Christabel
- B: Adela
- C: Emmeline
- D: Sylvia

You have won at least £32,000!

11) £64,000
Which Hitchcock film stars Sean Connery as a rich publisher?
- A: Rear Window
- B: Marnie
- C: The Birds
- D: Notorious

12) £125,000
Fava bean is an alternative name for which type of bean?
- A: Flageolet
- B: Kidney
- C: Broad
- D: Lima

13) £250,000
Which number golf club used to be called a 'mashie iron'?
- A: Two
- B: Three
- C: Four
- D: Five

14) £500,000
In 'Dangermouse', what was the name of the villain Baron Greenback's fluffy white pet?
- A: Augustus
- B: Caligula
- C: Nero
- D: Tiberius

15) £1,000,000
Which of these central American countries is the largest in area?
- A: Guatemala
- B: Honduras
- C: Nicaragua
- D: Panama

CONGRATULATIONS YOU ARE A MILLIONAIRE!

GAME 10 ANSWERS PAGE 60

50:50 from page 52
Ask The Audience from page 56
Phone-A-Friend

11

GAME 11

1) £100

When someone suddenly emerges from obscurity, they are said to come out of the what?

A: Needlework
B: Metalwork
C: Woodwork
D: Patchwork

2) £200

How is the company International Business Machines better known?

A: Microsoft
B: IBM
C: Apple
D: Dell

3) £300

Which road is known as the London Orbital Motorway?

A: M1
B: M4
C: M62
D: M25

4) £500

Which 'Bloggs' is another name for the average British man?

A: Jim
B: Jack
C: John
D: Joe

5) £1,000

Which of the following is a 2003 film directed by Clint Eastwood?

A: Ethereal Sea
B: Strange Stream
C: Mystic River
D: Weird Pool

You have won at least £1,000!

6) £2,000

Complete the title of the novel by William Thackeray, 'Vanity ...'?

A: Forest
B: Field
C: Fair
D: Farm

7) £4,000

Which of these is a suburb of Birmingham?

A: Selly Ash
B: Selly Elm
C: Selly Oak
D: Selly Fir

8) £8,000

Esholt, near Bradford, found fame as the location for which TV series?

A: Hollyoaks
B: Crossroads
C: Emmerdale
D: Heartbeat

9) £16,000

Emmenthal is a cheese originating from which country?

A: Germany
B: Italy
C: Belgium
D: Switzerland

10) £32,000

In which city is the musical 'The Beautiful Game' set?

A: Liverpool
B: Manchester
C: Belfast
D: London

You have won at least £32,000!

11) £64,000

Which star of the hit US sitcom 'Cheers' did Danny Devito marry?

A: Kirsty Alley
B: Shelley Long
C: Rhea Perlman
D: Bebe Neuwirth

12) £125,000

What was the former name of the Democratic Republic of the Congo?

A: Burundi
B: Zaire
C: Rwanda
D: Malawi

13) £250,000

In which card game is the object to score as close to nine as possible?

A: Rummy
B: Whist
C: Bèzique
D: Chemin de fer

14) £500,000

In which of the following does the cartoon character Spongebob Squarepants live?

A: Bikini Bottom
B: Atomic Atoll
C: Lilo Lagoon
D: Coral Canyon

15) £1,000,000

Who erected the Mausoleum at Halicarnassus, one of the Seven Wonders of the Ancient World?

A: Phidias
B: Mausolus
C: Artemisia
D: Ptolemy II

GAME 11 ANSWERS PAGE 61

50:50 from page 52
Ask The Audience from page 56
Phone-A-Friend

CONGRATULATIONS YOU ARE A MILLIONAIRE!

GAME 12

1) £100
Which of these traditionally comes before 'hooray' to introduce a cheer?
- A: Toe, toe
- B: Ear, ear
- C: Hip, hip
- D: Gum, gum

2) £200
What type of agency founded by Thomas Cook traces its roots back to the 1840s?
- A: News
- B: Employment
- C: Estate
- D: Travel

3) £300
Which of these is a shipping forecast area?
- A: Twenties
- B: Thirties
- C: Forties
- D: Fifties

4) £500
Which word completes a sailor's mock oath, 'Shiver my ...'?
- A: Timbers
- B: Rafters
- C: Planks
- D: Floor boards

5) £1,000
What was Reese Witherspoon in the title of two films?
- A: Legally Blonde
- B: Rightfully Red
- C: Justly Raven
- D: Lawfully Mousy

You have won at least £1,000!

6) £2,000
Which British city introduced a congestion charge in February 2003?
- A: Glasgow
- B: London
- C: Manchester
- D: Birmingham

7) £4,000
In which decade was the so-called 'Summer of Love'?
- A: 1920s
- B: 1930s
- C: 1950s
- D: 1960s

8) £8,000
Psychotherapists would be likely to use a 'primal' what in their works?
- A: Fear
- B: Instinct
- C: Reflex
- D: Scream

9) £16,000
Whose first novel was entitled 'Adam Bede'?
- A: Thomas Hardy
- B: George Eliot
- C: Wilkie Collins
- D: Anne Brontë

10) £32,000
In the musical 'Annie', what is the name of orphan Annie's dog?
- A: Paddy
- B: Sandy
- C: Timmy
- D: Whisky

You have won at least £32,000!

11) £64,000
On which TV show was Colin Farrell once a regular?
- A: Ballykissangel
- B: Hamish Macbeth
- C: Father Ted
- D: Taggart

12) £125,000
Which of these is a type of antelope?
- A: Koel
- B: Klipspringer
- C: Krait
- D: Kagu

13) £250,000
In which city was the US TV drama 'thirtysomething' set?
- A: Boston
- B: Chicago
- C: Baltimore
- D: Philadelphia

14) £500,000
Which ancient empire had a royal bodyguard of ten thousand men called the Immortals?
- A: Macedonian
- B: Babylonian
- C: Egyptian
- D: Persian

15) £1,000,000
In which sport are the Kinnaird Cup and the Jesters' Club Cup competed for?
- A: Real tennis
- B: Fives
- C: Polo
- D: Croquet

GAME 12 ANSWERS PAGE 61

50:50 from page 52
Ask The Audience from page 56
Phone-A-Friend

CONGRATULATIONS YOU ARE A MILLIONAIRE!

GAME 13

1) £100
What type of football match does not form part of a serious competition?
- A: Chummy
- B: Friendly
- C: Pally
- D: Matey

2) £200
Which of the following is a lay magistrate in the UK?
- A: MP
- B: VIP
- C: JP
- D: PC

3) £300
In the 1970s, feminists were said to burn which item to demonstrate their liberation?
- A: Nightdress
- B: Oven mitt
- C: Apron
- D: Bra

4) £500
What goes with 'movers' to refer to people with power and influence?
- A: Shakers
- B: Quakers
- C: Takers
- D: Bakers

5) £1,000
Complete the title of the 1994 film starring Tim Robbins and Morgan Freeman, 'The Shawshank ...'?
- A: Revelation
- B: Resurrection
- C: Redemption
- D: Renewal

You have won at least £1,000!

6) £2,000
Complete this Shakespeare line, 'A rose by any other name would ...'?
- A: Feel as soft
- B: Look as pretty
- C: Smell as sweet
- D: Grow as tall

7) £4,000
Which word comes after 'Oscar' in the NATO alphabet?
- A: Piper
- B: Peter
- C: Pointer
- D: Papa

8) £8,000
Which football team released a single entitled 'Blue Is The Colour'?
- A: Portsmouth
- B: Everton
- C: Coventry City
- D: Chelsea

9) £16,000
The cocktail known as Planter's Punch is made with which spirit?
- A: Gin
- B: Brandy
- C: Whisky
- D: Rum

10) £32,000
What is the name of the cafe in 'Frasier'?
- A: Cafe Senza
- B: Cafe Nervosa
- C: Cafe Delizia
- D: Cafe Fantazia

You have won at least £32,000!

11) £64,000
In which of these events might a technique called the Eastern cut-off have been used?
- A: Long jump
- B: Javelin
- C: Discus
- D: High jump

12) £125,000
In the Bible, where did Moses receive the Ten Commandments?
- A: Mount Carmel
- B: Mount Sinai
- C: Mount Ararat
- D: Mount Zion

13) £250,000
In which sport is the Stanley Cup competed for?
- A: Baseball
- B: Ice hockey
- C: Field hockey
- D: Tennis

14) £500,000
What shape is the recognition symbol on the 2004 issue Bank of England £10 note?
- A: Circle
- B: Diamond
- C: Square
- D: Triangle

15) £1,000,000
Which of these is a college at Durham University?
- A: Grey
- B: White
- C: Black
- D: Brown

GAME 13 ANSWERS PAGE 61

50:50 from page 52

Ask The Audience from page 56

Phone-A-Friend

CONGRATULATIONS YOU ARE A MILLIONAIRE!

GAME 14

1) £100

Which of these Latin phrases refers to dry land as opposed to water or the air?

- A: Terra sounder
- B: Terra safer
- C: Terra harder
- D: Terra firma

2) £200

Which phrase refers to a news story that has just occurred?

- A: Snapping news
- B: Cracking news
- C: Splitting news
- D: Breaking news

3) £300

Which of these many-limbed creatures is represented in the zodiac?

- A: Spider
- B: Octopus
- C: Crab
- D: Millipede

4) £500

Which of these is an informal term for the Atlantic Ocean?

- A: The Lake
- B: The Pond
- C: The River
- D: The Stream

5) £1,000

What is the meaning of the French word 'rue'?

- A: Mountain
- B: Bread
- C: Ice cream
- D: Street

You have won at least £1,000!

6) £2,000

Who regularly presents a lunchtime TV show with Des O'Connor?

- A: Melanie Sykes
- B: Cat Deeley
- C: Donna Air
- D: Edith Bowman

7) £4,000

In a famous poem, Minnehaha is the wife of which character?

- A: Beowulf
- B: Sir Lancelot
- C: Robin Hood
- D: Hiawatha

8) £8,000

Althorp is the seat of which family?

- A: Beaufort
- B: Cavendish
- C: Percy
- D: Spencer

9) £16,000

On a French menu, what is an 'andouillette'?

- A: Chocolate cake
- B: Sausage
- C: Cheese tart
- D: Sauce

10) £32,000

From which country does the wine known as Bull's Blood originate?

- A: Turkey
- B: Spain
- C: Hungary
- D: Italy

You have won at least £32,000!

11) £64,000

From which country does the electronic pop act Royksopp originate?

- A: Sweden
- B: Norway
- C: Denmark
- D: Finland

12) £125,000

Which children's programme featured the characters Aunt Flo and Farmer Barleymow?

- A: Bod
- B: Bagpuss
- C: Andy Pandy
- D: The Flumps

13) £250,000

Which European capital city is situated on the island of Sjaelland?

- A: Oslo
- B: Helsinki
- C: Copenhagen
- D: Stockholm

14) £500,000

Which English monarch did Antony Babington plot to murder in the 16th century?

- A: Henry VIII
- B: Elizabeth I
- C: Edward VI
- D: Mary I

15) £1,000,000

Which of these British prime ministers did not attend Eton and Oxford?

- A: Macmillan
- B: Heath
- C: Eden
- D: Douglas-Home

GAME 14 ANSWERS PAGE 61

50:50 from page 52

Ask The Audience from page 56

Phone-A-Friend

CONGRATULATIONS YOU ARE A MILLIONAIRE!

15

GAME 15

1) £100
If you let someone begin a race before you, what have you given them?
- A: Foot start
- B: Hand start
- C: Arm start
- D: Head start

2) £200
What is the name of the shelter beside a sports field, where the coach sits during the game?
- A: Buyout
- B: Fallout
- C: Knockout
- D: Dugout

3) £300
Which would you not expect to find in a pack of playing cards?
- A: Clubs
- B: Spades
- C: Diamonds
- D: Sapphires

4) £500
Which name goes before 'dazzler' to describe something attractive?
- A: Tommy
- B: Bobby
- C: Sammy
- D: Jimmy

5) £1,000
'Pomme' is the French word for which fruit?
- A: Cherry
- B: Apple
- C: Peach
- D: Lemon

You have won at least £1,000!

6) £2,000
The zebra is native to which continent?
- A: Africa
- B: Asia
- C: South America
- D: Australia

7) £4,000
Which TV cook set up the restaurant 'Fifteen'?
- A: Nigella Lawson
- B: Gordon Ramsay
- C: Delia Smith
- D: Jamie Oliver

8) £8,000
What is the first name of the Queen's nephew Lord Linley?
- A: Michael
- B: David
- C: Stephen
- D: Alexander

9) £16,000
Which of these is a college at Oxford University?
- A: Exeter
- B: Enfield
- C: Edinburgh
- D: Epping

10) £32,000
Which word refers to the breeding grounds of penguins?
- A: Snuggeries
- B: Catteries
- C: Coteries
- D: Rookeries

You have won at least £32,000!

11) £64,000
From which city did the 1980s group ABC come?
- A: Manchester
- B: Sheffield
- C: Stoke
- D: Liverpool

12) £125,000
In 2004, Michelle Wie became famous as a teenage prodigy in which sport?
- A: Golf
- B: Tennis
- C: Darts
- D: Swimming

13) £250,000
The maximum dimensions of which of these sports courts are 20ft x 44ft?
- A: Tennis
- B: Squash
- C: Badminton
- D: Pelota

14) £500,000
Which bird features on the reverse of the Bank of England £10 note with Charles Darwin?
- A: Stormy petrel
- B: Albatross
- C: Pelican
- D: Hummingbird

15) £1,000,000
What would normally be collected in a Nansen bottle?
- A: Insects
- B: Sea Water
- C: Gases
- D: Pills

GAME 15 ANSWERS PAGE 61

50:50 from page 52

Ask The Audience from page 56

Phone-A-Friend

CONGRATULATIONS YOU ARE A MILLIONAIRE!

16

1) £100

The small perceptible part of a larger situation is known as the 'tip of the ...'?

- A: Icebox
- B: Iceberg
- C: Ice cube
- D: Ice house

2) £200

What name is given to a sudden spell of decidedly cooler weather?

- A: Cold snap
- B: Cold flap
- C: Cold slap
- D: Cold crack

3) £300

Which is the smallest and least powerful piece on a chessboard?

- A: Bishop
- B: Knight
- C: Rook
- D: Pawn

4) £500

Which was not one of the 'Road' films starring Bob Hope and Bing Crosby?

- A: Road to Bali
- B: Road to Utopia
- C: Road to Rio
- D: Road to Wales

5) £1,000

What is the Latin word meaning 'queen'?

- A: Regent
- B: Regina
- C: Regime
- D: Regiment

You have won at least £1,000!

6) £2,000

Which of these is a song from the musical 'West Side Story'?

- A: Canada
- B: Mexico
- C: America
- D: Panama

7) £4,000

Which dance is featured in the musical 'The Rocky Horror Show'?

- A: Time Bomb
- B: Time Capsule
- C: Time Limit
- D: Time Warp

8) £8,000

Which popular computer game involves interlocking different body shapes?

- A: Minesweeper
- B: Jezzball
- C: Alchemy
- D: Tetris

9) £16,000

In which Italian city is the Pitti Palace?

- A: Rome
- B: Venice
- C: Florence
- D: Turin

10) £32,000

Alf is a nickname of which of these singers?

- A: Alannah Myles
- B: Alicia Keyes
- C: Avril Levigne
- D: Alison Moyet

You have won at least £32,000!

11) £64,000

Who wrote the children's classic 'Nightbirds in Nantucket'?

- A: A A Milne
- B: Joan Aiken
- C: Roald Dahl
- D: Nina Bawden

12) £125,000

'The Happy Prince and Other Tales' was written by whom?

- A: Oscar Wilde
- B: James Joyce
- C: Brendan Behan
- D: Samuel Beckett

13) £250,000

Which wine bottle holds the most?

- A: Jeroboam
- B: Balthazar
- C: Magnum
- D: Rehoboam

14) £500,000

At 74 kilometres in length, which is the longest line on the London Underground?

- A: Metropolitan
- B: District
- C: Central
- D: Piccadilly

15) £1,000,000

What colour ribbon supports the Order of the Thistle?

- A: White
- B: Green
- C: Blue
- D: Crimson

GAME 16 ANSWERS PAGE 61

50:50 from page 52

Ask The Audience from page 56

Phone-A-Friend

CONGRATULATIONS YOU ARE A MILLIONAIRE!

1) £100
Which of these phrases refers to hitting a target in close proximity?
- A: Point-blank
- B: Point-blunt
- C: Point-blink
- D: Point-blurt

2) £200
Which of these refers to rich, famous and fashionable celebrities?
- A: Bitterati
- B: Litterati
- C: Glitterati
- D: Flitterati

3) £300
Which of these is a popular type of cheese?
- A: Swedish yellow
- B: Norwegian grey
- C: Finnish red
- D: Danish blue

4) £500
Which of these James Bond film characters is most likely to say 'Now pay attention, 007!'?
- A: Goldfinger
- B: Q
- C: Oddjob
- D: Pussy Galore

5) £1,000
In which US state are the cities of San Diego and San Francisco?
- A: Washington
- B: Texas
- C: Maine
- D: California

You have won at least £1,000!

6) £2,000
How does the name of the Alpine peak, Mont Blanc, translate into English?
- A: High Mountain
- B: White Mountain
- C: Snow Mountain
- D: Cold Mountain

7) £4,000
Ecosse is French for which country?
- A: England
- B: Ireland
- C: Scotland
- D: Wales

8) £8,000
Which of these is a sliding effect in music?
- A: Pizzicato
- B: Arpeggio
- C: Glissando
- D: Decrescendo

9) £16,000
In Victorian England, what was a fingersmith?
- A: Pianist
- B: Postman
- C: Pickpocket
- D: Policeman

10) £32,000
Clifford Price is the real name of which recording artist?
- A: Suggs
- B: Seal
- C: Bono
- D: Goldie

You have won at least £32,000!

11) £64,000
What was the first name of the great-granddaughter of Charles Dickens, also an author?
- A: Angela
- B: Monica
- C: Jennifer
- D: Anna

12) £125,000
Which of these was a Roman poet and satirist who lived in the first century BC?
- A: Hilary
- B: Horace
- C: Hamish
- D: Hector

13) £250,000
Who was the first English monarch to declare himself King of Ireland?
- A: William I
- B: Henry VIII
- C: Edward III
- D: Charles II

14) £500,000
Which of the following does Charlotte Rampling play in the 2003 film 'Swimming Pool'?
- A: Author
- B: Doctor
- C: Lawyer
- D: Architect

15) £1,000,000
What code name was given to the Dunkirk evacuations of 1940?
- A: Sanctuary
- B: Digger
- C: Juno
- D: Dynamo

GAME 17 ANSWERS PAGE 61

50:50 from page 52

Ask The Audience from page 56

Phone-A-Friend

CONGRATULATIONS YOU ARE A MILLIONAIRE!

GAME 18

1) £100
What is the usual colour of a ripe lemon?
- A: Blue
- B: Red
- C: Yellow
- D: Pink

2) £200
Which of these is both a slang word for a bullet and a creature found in the garden?
- A: Rug
- B: Mug
- C: Slug
- D: Thug

3) £300
An aperitif is usually drunk before doing what?
- A: Going to bed
- B: Eating a meal
- C: Fencing
- D: Exercising

4) £500
Complete the title of the 1999 award-winning film, 'Crouching Tiger, ...'?
- A: Lost Unicorn
- B: Mislaid Sphinx
- C: Hidden Dragon
- D: Secret Serpent

5) £1,000
In which city is Times Square?
- A: Tokyo
- B: Cairo
- C: Birmingham
- D: New York

You have won at least £1,000!

6) £2,000
The French game pétanque most closely resembles which game, popular in Britain?
- A: Darts
- B: Bowls
- C: Snooker
- D: Croquet

7) £4,000
Which of these soups is traditionally served cold?
- A: Scotch broth
- B: Minestrone
- C: Vichyssoise
- D: Mulligatawny

8) £8,000
If something is described as postprandial, it takes place after what?
- A: A bath
- B: Death
- C: Birth
- D: A meal

9) £16,000
Which country will host the 2007 Rugby World Cup finals?
- A: Italy
- B: Samoa
- C: Romania
- D: France

10) £32,000
Ochlophobia is a fear of what?
- A: Snakes
- B: Thunder
- C: Crowds
- D: Punishment

You have won at least £32,000!

11) £64,000
In classical mythology, into what did Athena turn Arachne?
- A: Swan
- B: Snake
- C: Stone
- D: Spider

12) £125,000
Which of these is not the title of a book in the New Testament?
- A: Colossians
- B: Hebrews
- C: Galileans
- D: Philippians

13) £250,000
Which Daily Mail cartoonist received an MBE in the 2004 New Year's Honours?
- A: Mahood
- B: Mac
- C: Matt
- D: Mike

14) £500,000
In which US state is the city of Chattanooga?
- A: Florida
- B: Montana
- C: Washington
- D: Tennessee

15) £1,000,000
To whom does Rudyard Kipling address each of his 'Just So Stories'?
- A: Dearly Beloved
- B: Dear Friend
- C: Best Beloved
- D: The Curious

GAME 18 ANSWERS PAGE 61

50:50 from page 52

Ask The Audience from page 56

Phone-A-Friend

CONGRATULATIONS YOU ARE A MILLIONAIRE!

GAME 19

1) £100
Which phrase decribes a police officer who does not wear a uniform?
- A: Drab clothes
- B: Plain clothes
- C: Ugly clothes
- D: Old clothes

2) £200
In a village, what is most likely to be known as the 'local'?
- A: Church
- B: School
- C: Pond
- D: Pub

3) £300
Which of these is a spicy condiment?
- A: Kidney
- B: Whitney
- C: Rodney
- D: Chutney

4) £500
What are awarded to actors honoured on the Hollywood Walk of Fame?
- A: Hearts
- B: Stars
- C: Diamonds
- D: Masks

5) £1,000
In which country is the region of Andalusia?
- A: Italy
- B: France
- C: Portugal
- D: Spain

You have won at least £1,000!

6) £2,000
In which country is the Palace of Versailles?
- A: Belgium
- B: Canada
- C: France
- D: Austria

7) £4,000
Which suit in a pack of cards is denoted by a trefoil shape?
- A: Clubs
- B: Spades
- C: Hearts
- D: Diamonds

8) £8,000
What is the surname of Duncan from the former band, Blue?
- A: James
- B: Webbe
- C: Ryan
- D: Costa

9) £16,000
Which of these delicacies is a speciality of the Perigord region of France?
- A: Truffles
- B: Caviar
- C: Oysters
- D: Champagne

10) £32,000
Which of these countries does not have land on the island of Borneo?
- A: Indonesia
- B: Brunei
- C: Malaysia
- D: China

You have won at least £32,000!

11) £64,000
In 'Gulliver's Travels', which land is the kingdom of the giants?
- A: Lilliput
- B: Brobdingnag
- C: Laputa
- D: Lagado

12) £125,000
What nationality is the racing driver Nick Heidfeld?
- A: Danish
- B: German
- C: Finnish
- D: Dutch

13) £250,000
In which of these countries is it not customary to drive on the left-hand side of the road?
- A: India
- B: Australia
- C: Japan
- D: Canada

14) £500,000
Which European river flows through a gorge known as the Iron Gate?
- A: Rhine
- B: Danube
- C: Volga
- D: Vistula

15) £1,000,000
What is Lady Chatterley's first name in the novel by D H Lawrence?
- A: Lavinia
- B: Violet
- C: Constance
- D: Prudence

GAME 19 ANSWERS PAGE 61

50:50 from page 52
Ask The Audience from page 56
Phone-A-Friend

CONGRATULATIONS YOU ARE A MILLIONAIRE!

GAME 20

1) £100
In children's stories, how many wishes are traditionally granted by a genie or a fairy?
- A: One
- B: Two
- C: Three
- D: Four

2) £200
Which of these is the nautical term for the rear of a ship?
- A: Harsh
- B: Severe
- C: Stern
- D: Strict

3) £300
Which part of the tea plant is used to make the popular beverage?
- A: Oil
- B: Bark
- C: Root
- D: Leaf

4) £500
Which 2000 romantic comedy film is based on a bestselling novel by Joanne Harris?
- A: Chocolat
- B: Fromage
- C: Café
- D: Petit pain

5) £1,000
Which of these is a town in West Sussex?
- A: Wolverhampton
- B: Northampton
- C: Southampton
- D: Littlehampton

You have won at least £1,000!

6) £2,000
Which of these Australian mammals has webbed feet?
- A: Wombat
- B: Kangaroo
- C: Platypus
- D: Koala

7) £4,000
Larnaca is a town on which Mediterranean island?
- A: Cyprus
- B: Sicily
- C: Corsica
- D: Sardinia

8) £8,000
The word auricular refers to which part of the human body?
- A: Foot
- B: Knee
- C: Ear
- D: Wrist

9) £16,000
Who plays Huggy Bear in the 2004 film version of 'Starsky and Hutch'?
- A: Dr Dre
- B: Snoop Dog
- C: LL Cool J
- D: P Diddy

10) £32,000
Which branch of mathematics takes its name from the Latin for 'pebble'?
- A: Algebra
- B: Trigonometry
- C: Geometry
- D: Calculus

You have won at least £32,000!

11) £64,000
Which is a college at Cambridge University?
- A: Darwin
- B: Newton
- C: Faraday
- D: Cavendish

12) £125,000
What name was given to an Indian soldier in the British Army?
- A: Gurkha
- B: Adjutant
- C: Pathan
- D: Sepoy

13) £250,000
In which sci-fi TV series did aliens come to Earth from Sirius?
- A: UFO
- B: Quatermass
- C: V
- D: The Invaders

14) £500,000
In which European country is the parliament known as the Vouli?
- A: Greece
- B: Italy
- C: Albania
- D: Finland

15) £1,000,000
Who recorded the first ever single to reach No 1 in the British pop charts?
- A: Eddie Fisher
- B: Guy Mitchell
- C: Al Martino
- D: Doris Day

GAME 20 ANSWERS PAGE 61

50:50 from page 52
Ask The Audience from page 56
Phone-A-Friend

CONGRATULATIONS YOU ARE A MILLIONAIRE!

GAME 21

1) £100
A bottle of which alcoholic drink is traditionally used to launch a ship?
- A: Sherry
- B: Brandy
- C: Gin
- D: Champagne

2) £200
Which of the following means a group of islands?
- A: A cappella
- B: Archipelago
- C: Achilles
- D: Armadillo

3) £300
Which of the following names relates to a jug used for drinking beer?
- A: Dave
- B: Mike
- C: Steve
- D: Toby

4) £500
On which river does the city of Cairo stand?
- A: Amazon
- B: Nile
- C: Ganges
- D: Thames

5) £1,000
In which county is the holiday resort of St Ives?
- A: Devon
- B: Cornwall
- C: Kent
- D: Dorset

You have won at least £1,000!

6) £2,000
The TV series 'Holby City' is a spin-off from which other medical drama?
- A: Bodies
- B: A&E
- C: Casualty
- D: ER

7) £4,000
A representative of which country won the World Idol contest on New Year's Day, 2004?
- A: Germany
- B: Norway
- C: UK
- D: South Africa

8) £8,000
What is the name of Bob the Builder's cat?
- A: Pilchard
- B: Kipper
- C: Mackerel
- D: Sardine

9) £16,000
Queen Rania is the queen of which country?
- A: Morocco
- B: Kuwait
- C: Jordan
- D: Bahrain

10) £32,000
The Briton Mark Lewis-Francis is a famous name in which sport?
- A: Athletics
- B: Snooker
- C: Football
- D: Hockey

You have won at least £32,000!

11) £64,000
How many counters does each player have at the start of a game of backgammon?
- A: Ten
- B: Twelve
- C: Fifteen
- D: Twenty

12) £125,000
What colour shirts did Garibaldi and his followers wear?
- A: Brown
- B: Black
- C: Red
- D: Blue

13) £250,000
As of 2004, whose only UK No 1 single was 'Fly Away' in 1999?
- A: Lenny Kravitz
- B: LA Guns
- C: Chris Rea
- D: Shabba Ranks

14) £500,000
What part of a Roman soldier's equipment was the pilum?
- A: Shield
- B: Sword
- C: Javelin
- D: Helmet

15) £1,000,000
Which sport was invented in 1898 by a child called Frank Beal?
- A: Badminton
- B: Bowls
- C: Paddle Tennis
- D: Curling

GAME 21 ANSWERS PAGE 62

50:50 from page 52
Ask The Audience from page 56
Phone-A-Friend

CONGRATULATIONS YOU ARE A MILLIONAIRE!

1) £100
Which of these is a gambling device, often found in pubs?
- A: Veg machine
- B: Spice machine
- C: Herb machine
- D: Fruit machine

2) £200
Complete the title of the song from 'Snow White and the Seven Dwarfs', 'Whistle While You ...'?
- A: Wait
- B: Walk
- C: Work
- D: Weld

3) £300
To what kind of shop would you take a prescription?
- A: Draper
- B: Tailor
- C: Grocer
- D: Chemist

4) £500
In which county is the Lake District?
- A: Cumbria
- B: Devon
- C: Kent
- D: Norfolk

5) £1,000
Usually, what type of drink is 'home brew'?
- A: Beer
- B: Coffee
- C: Gin
- D: Whisky

You have won at least £1,000!

6) £2,000
What does the German word 'danke' mean?
- A: Yes
- B: No
- C: Please
- D: Thank you

7) £4,000
In 1581, Sir Francis Drake became mayor of which city?
- A: Hull
- B: Glasgow
- C: Plymouth
- D: Bristol

8) £8,000
Campanula is the Latin name for which flower?
- A: Blue poppy
- B: Buttercup
- C: Busy Lizzie
- D: Bellflower

9) £16,000
Which golfer is known as the 'Big Easy'?
- A: Ernie Els
- B: Tiger Woods
- C: Ian Woosnam
- D: Sergio Garcia

10) £32,000
The footballer Harry Kewell married which 'Emmerdale' star in 2002?
- A: Sheree Murphy
- B: Emma Atkins
- C: Leah Bracknell
- D: Vicky Binns

You have won at least £32,000!

11) £64,000
In ancient Persia, what was a magus?
- A: Teacher
- B: Soothsayer
- C: Warlord
- D: Priest

12) £125,000
In which year did the General Strike take place in the UK?
- A: 1906
- B: 1926
- C: 1929
- D: 1936

13) £250,000
Which regular character from the TV series is killed off in the film 'Star Trek: Nemesis'?
- A: Worf
- B: Riker
- C: La Forge
- D: Data

14) £500,000
What is the name of the Egyptian jackel-headed god?
- A: Anubis
- B: Isis
- C: Osiris
- D: Horus

15) £1,000,000
Which planet is sometimes known as Lucifer?
- A: Jupiter
- B: Mercury
- C: Venus
- D: Pluto

GAME 22 ANSWERS PAGE 62

50:50 from page 52
Ask The Audience from page 56
Phone-A-Friend

CONGRATULATIONS YOU ARE A MILLIONAIRE!

GAME 23

1) £100
Which is generally considered to be the coldest season of the year?
- A: Spring
- B: Summer
- C: Autumn
- D: Winter

2) £200
The Latin phrase 'nil desperandum' means 'never ...'?
- A: Destroy
- B: Disagree
- C: Deserve
- D: Despair

3) £300
Which of these mythological beings are most associated with helping Father Christmas?
- A: Trolls
- B: Dragons
- C: Elves
- D: Werewolves

4) £500
Which of these is a dish of duck, scallions and hoisin sauce?
- A: Tokyo duck
- B: Peking duck
- C: Bangkok duck
- D: Delhi duck

5) £1,000
Which item of confectionery is known in the USA as 'cotton candy'?
- A: Toffee apple
- B: Candyfloss
- C: Fudge
- D: Chewing gum

You have won at least £1,000!

6) £2,000
What was the name of Tina Turner's husband who sang with her on 'River Deep Mountain High'?
- A: Otis
- B: Marvin
- C: Ike
- D: Isaac

7) £4,000
What does the musical instruction 'lento' mean?
- A: Quick
- B: Loud
- C: Slow
- D: Quiet

8) £8,000
Faliraki is a popular tourist resort on which Greek island?
- A: Rhodes
- B: Corfu
- C: Crete
- D: Mykonos

9) £16,000
Which of these is the name for a cut of beef?
- A: Dress
- B: Robe
- C: Slip
- D: Skirt

10) £32,000
Which racehorse won the Cheltenham Gold Cup in three consecutive years in the 1960s?
- A: Mill Reef
- B: Nijinsky
- C: Arkle
- D: Aldaniti

You have won at least £32,000!

11) £64,000
In which African country is the Serengeti National Park?
- A: Tanzania
- B: Kenya
- C: Botswana
- D: Zimbabwe

12) £125,000
Which of these words means wickedness?
- A: Tortuosity
- B: Turpitude
- C: Torpidity
- D: Torridity

13) £250,000
What colour is the 5-euro bank note?
- A: Grey
- B: Blue
- C: Green
- D: Pink

14) £500,000
Herzog was the Holy Roman Empire's equivalent of which rank?
- A: Duke
- B: Marquess
- C: Viscount
- D: Count

15) £1,000,000
Which flying machine takes its name from the Greek for 'self' and 'circle'?
- A: Autogiro
- B: Dirigible
- C: Aeroplane
- D: Helicopter

GAME 23 ANSWERS PAGE 62

50:50 from page 52
Ask The Audience from page 56
Phone-A-Friend

CONGRATULATIONS YOU ARE A MILLIONAIRE!

24

GAME 24

1) £100
What number code is required to withdraw money from a bank using a cashcard?
- A: NEEDLE
- B: PIN
- C: THIMBLE
- D: THREAD

2) £200
On which continent is the geographical South Pole?
- A: South America
- B: Australia
- C: Antarctica
- D: Asia

3) £300
With which of these is Robin Hood most associated?
- A: Catapult
- B: Peashooter
- C: Bow and arrow
- D: Tomahawk

4) £500
Which of these is an important ingredient in sushi?
- A: Potato
- B: Ravioli
- C: Bread
- D: Rice

5) £1,000
A taverna is a traditional restaurant or café in which country?
- A: Greece
- B: France
- C: Italy
- D: Spain

You have won at least £1,000!

6) £2,000
What is the name for the style in which hair is braided into parallel plaits?
- A: Corn rows
- B: Potato rows
- C: Rice rows
- D: Wheat rows

7) £4,000
In which country is Soave wine produced?
- A: Germany
- B: Italy
- C: France
- D: Spain

8) £8,000
At which location is Frogmore, where Queen Victoria and Prince Albert are buried?
- A: Balmoral
- B: Sandringham
- C: Isle of Wight
- D: Windsor

9) £16,000
Venus is the Roman equivalent of which Greek Goddess?
- A: Athene
- B: Persephone
- C: Aphrodite
- D: Artemis

10) £32,000
Which letter is not used as a symbol for a chemical element?
- A: I
- B: E
- C: O
- D: U

You have won at least £32,000!

11) £64,000
What is the meaning of Uluru, the aboriginal name for Ayers Rock?
- A: Great pebble
- B: Sacred place
- C: Citadel
- D: Big table

12) £125,000
Which actress married Eric Benet in 2001?
- A: Angela Bassett
- B: Jada Pinkett
- C: Angelina Jolie
- D: Halle Berry

13) £250,000
Which US state was named for the brother of Charles II of England?
- A: Georgia
- B: New York
- C: Vermont
- D: Delaware

14) £500,000
Which 18th century battle was fought on Drumossie Moor?
- A: Culloden
- B: Falkirk
- C: Prestonpans
- D: Stirling

15) £1,000,000
Which of these is a chemical element?
- A: Bofnium
- B: Dilithium
- C: Ytterbium
- D: Calatrium

CONGRATULATIONS YOU ARE A MILLIONAIRE!

GAME 24 ANSWERS PAGE 62

50:50 from page 52
Ask The Audience from page 56
Phone-A-Friend

25

GAME 25

1) £100
Which of these is not part of a traditional English breakfast?
- A: Sausages
- B: Eggs
- C: Bacon
- D: Spaghetti

2) £200
Which dynasty, famous for its porcelain, ruled China from 1368 to 1644?
- A: Ping
- B: Pong
- C: Ting
- D: Ming

3) £300
How many bags full of wool does Baa Baa Black Sheep have in the nursery rhyme?
- A: Three
- B: Four
- C: Five
- D: Six

4) £500
In alphabet soup, the letters are made up from pieces of what?
- A: Carrot
- B: Pasta
- C: Chicken
- D: Bread

5) £1,000
A dish traditionally eaten on Thanksgiving Day in the USA is pumpkin ...?
- A: Salad
- B: Crumble
- C: Pie
- D: Stew

You have won at least £1,000!

6) £2,000
If the 1960s were 'Swinging', how were the 1920s traditionally described?
- A: Rocking
- B: Rolling
- C: Roaring
- D: Rollicking

7) £4,000
In which of these sports do you 'peg out' with the final stroke of the game?
- A: Table tennis
- B: Croquet
- C: Polo
- D: Squash

8) £8,000
What is the setting for the US TV comedy 'Scrubs'?
- A: Prison
- B: Restaurant
- C: Hospital
- D: School

9) £16,000
Which of these TV characters drove a yellow vintage car called Bessie?
- A: Doctor Kildare
- B: Doctor Quinn
- C: Doctor Finlay
- D: Doctor Who

10) £32,000
Which is the watery by-product produced in cheese-making?
- A: Curds
- B: Lees
- C: Whey
- D: Buttermilk

You have won at least £32,000!

11) £64,000
Which London park is surrounded by the Outer Circle?
- A: Regent's Park
- B: St James' Park
- C: Hyde Park
- D: Greenwich Park

12) £125,000
The international governing body of which sport is the FISA?
- A: Rowing
- B: Rackets
- C: Real Tennis
- D: Rounders

13) £250,000
Which of these Australian cities is the most northerly?
- A: Brisbane
- B: Newcastle
- C: Adelaide
- D: Perth

14) £500,000
Which is Britain's largest Anglican cathedral?
- A: Coventry
- B: Liverpool
- C: Winchester
- D: Canterbury

15) £1,000,000
Krung Threp is the official name of which eastern capital city?
- A: Manila
- B: Hanoi
- C: Bangkok
- D: Seoul

CONGRATULATIONS YOU ARE A MILLIONAIRE!

GAME 25 ANSWERS PAGE 62

50:50 from page 52
Ask The Audience from page 56
Phone-A-Friend

26

GAME 26

1) £100
What is the usual colour of garden peas?
- A: Blue
- B: Green
- C: Red
- D: White

2) £200
Which of the following is a hand in poker?
- A: Royal icing
- B: Royal blue
- C: Royal flush
- D: Royal warrant

3) £300
Which test determines worth, trust and reliability?
- A: Eye
- B: Litmus
- C: Acid
- D: Driving

4) £500
What kind of food is a bloomer?
- A: Ham
- B: Bread
- C: Cheese
- D: Fruit

5) £1,000
The newspaper Le Monde is published in which country?
- A: France
- B: Germany
- C: Italy
- D: Spain

You have won at least £1,000!

6) £2,000
Which of these creatures is well-known for felling trees using its large teeth?
- A: Badger
- B: Baboon
- C: Bison
- D: Beaver

7) £4,000
Which of these is a Spanish word for cowboy?
- A: Tapas
- B: Vaquero
- C: Siesta
- D: Conquistador

8) £8,000
What is described in a famous poem by Keats as 'Season of mists and mellow fruitfulness'?
- A: Spring
- B: Summer
- C: Autumn
- D: Winter

9) £16,000
Kernow is the Celtic name for which English county?
- A: Cumbria
- B: Cornwall
- C: Cheshire
- D: Cambridgeshire

10) £32,000
What number is denoted by the prefix 'dodeca-'?
- A: Ten
- B: Eight
- C: Twelve
- D: Twenty-four

You have won at least £32,000!

11) £64,000
How is the title character Carmen killed in Bizet's opera?
- A: Poisoned
- B: Hanged
- C: Drowned
- D: Stabbed

12) £125,000
Who played Sapphire in the TV sci-fi series 'Sapphire and Steel'?
- A: Honor Blackman
- B: Linda Thorson
- C: Joanna Lumley
- D: Diana Rigg

13) £250,000
Who is the Roman equivalent of the Greek god Cronus?
- A: Mars
- B: Vulcan
- C: Saturn
- D: Uranus

14) £500,000
In which field would Napier's bones have been helpful?
- A: Music
- B: Mathematics
- C: Medicine
- D: Millinery

15) £1,000,000
Which King of England is the origin of the expression 'Silly Billy'?
- A: William I
- B: William II
- C: William III
- D: William IV

GAME 26
ANSWERS
PAGE 62

50:50
from page 52

Ask The Audience
from page 56

Phone-A-Friend

CONGRATULATIONS YOU ARE A MILLIONAIRE!

GAME 27

1) £100
Which of these is a large island in the northern hemisphere?
- A: Blackland
- B: Redland
- C: Pinkland
- D: Greenland

2) £200
Which of these is a type of restaurant, specialising in meat dishes?
- A: Leglodge
- B: Chopcottage
- C: Ribmanor
- D: Steakhouse

3) £300
Someone in a bad mood is said to have 'got out of the wrong side of the ...'?
- A: Bath
- B: Bed
- C: Bunk
- D: Bar

4) £500
Who are the traditional enemies of Asterix the Gaul?
- A: Romans
- B: Russians
- C: Mexicans
- D: Turks

5) £1,000
In the rhyme, where was I going when I met a man who was seven-times married?
- A: St Austell
- B: St Albans
- C: St Ives
- D: St Just

You have won at least £1,000!

6) £2,000
Which of these musical titles features in the rhyme 'London Bridge is Falling Down'?
- A: Hello Dolly
- B: Kiss Me Kate
- C: Me and My Girl
- D: My Fair Lady

7) £4,000
Which football ground is Scotland's national stadium?
- A: Celtic Park
- B: Hampden Park
- C: Pittodrie
- D: Ibrox

8) £8,000
Which of these is a seabird?
- A: Snipe
- B: Skua
- C: Swift
- D: Swallow

9) £16,000
Which of these is the coldest planet in our Solar System?
- A: Jupiter
- B: Pluto
- C: Saturn
- D: Uranus

10) £32,000
Who addressed his sonnets to the 'Dark Lady'?
- A: Keats
- B: Byron
- C: Shakespeare
- D: Spencer

You have won at least £32,000!

11) £64,000
The Kikuyu is a native tribe of which African country?
- A: Zambia
- B: Zimbabwe
- C: Nigeria
- D: Kenya

12) £125,000
Which of these capital cities stands at the mouth of the River Plate?
- A: Lima
- B: Brasilia
- C: Montevideo
- D: Quito

13) £250,000
What is the first name of Caroline Aherne's TV character Mrs Merton?
- A: Dorothy
- B: Doris
- C: Mavis
- D: Primrose

14) £500,000
Which of the following is a unit of acceleration?
- A: Newton
- B: Galileo
- C: Einstein
- D: Watt

15) £1,000,000
Which architect designed the Cenotaph in London?
- A: Charles Barry
- B: Augustus Pugin
- C: Edwin Lutyens
- D: Gilbert Scott

GAME 27 ANSWERS PAGE 62

50:50 from page 52
Ask The Audience from page 56
Phone-A-Friend

CONGRATULATIONS YOU ARE A MILLIONAIRE!

GAME 28

1) £100

What is a special uniform worn by a servant or official called?

- A: Liverish
- B: Lively
- C: Livery
- D: Liverpool

2) £200

Which of these is a section of an orange or grapefruit?

- A: Fragment
- B: Pigment
- C: Segment
- D: Figment

3) £300

To which section of the orchestra does the oboe belong?

- A: Strings
- B: Brass
- C: Woodwind
- D: Percussion

4) £500

Complete the TV presenter David Dickinson's famous catchphrase, 'Cheap as ...'?

- A: Chops
- B: Chowder
- C: Chips
- D: Chilli

5) £1,000

Which of these instruments is popularly known as a 'squeeze box'?

- A: Harmonium
- B: Bagpipes
- C: Mouth organ
- D: Accordion

You have won at least £1000!

6) £2,000

'We Are The Champions' was a hit single for which band in 1977?

- A: Slade
- B: Queen
- C: Pink Floyd
- D: Deep Purple

7) £4,000

What nationality is the tennis player Jennifer Capriati?

- A: French
- B: Italian
- C: Spanish
- D: American

8) £8,000

Which country is known as Bharat in its own language?

- A: India
- B: Japan
- C: Finland
- D: Switzerland

9) £16,000

Which of these stately homes is in Bedfordshire?

- A: Longleat
- B: Harewood
- C: Woburn
- D: Badminton

10) £32,000

In classical mythology, what colour was the blood of the gods?

- A: Blue
- B: Purple
- C: Colourless
- D: Gold

You have won at least £32,000!

11) £64,000

Which ancient poet wrote the 'Aeneid'?

- A: Virgil
- B: Homer
- C: Aesop
- D: Ovid

12) £125,000

In which film did Ewan McGregor make his big screen debut?

- A: Being Human
- B: Shallow Grave
- C: Trainspotting
- D: Blue Juice

13) £250,000

Charon is the moon of which planet?

- A: Saturn
- B: Jupiter
- C: Pluto
- D: Uranus

14) £500,000

Which English poet wrote the poem 'Kubla Khan'?

- A: Milton
- B: Keats
- C: Coleridge
- D: Wordsworth

15) £1,000,000

Of what is limnology the study?

- A: Brasses
- B: Lakes
- C: Ferns
- D: Manuscripts

GAME 28 ANSWERS PAGE 62

50:50 from page 52
Ask The Audience from page 56
Phone-A-Friend

CONGRATULATIONS YOU ARE A MILLIONAIRE!

GAME 29

1) £100
What is the name given to the administrative head of a university or college?
- A: Dan
- B: Dean
- C: David
- D: Dudley

2) £200
Kissing which stone is said to bestow powers of persuasion?
- A: Rosetta
- B: Pumice
- C: Blarney
- D: Sharon

3) £300
Which of these is the chief female singer in an opera company?
- A: Prima quine
- B: Prima vera
- C: Prima facie
- D: Prima donna

4) £500
James Fenimore Cooper wrote 'The Last of the ...'?
- A: Skinheads
- B: Crew cuts
- C: Mullets
- D: Mohicans

5) £1,000
Who had a 2002 hit with 'The Ketchup Song'?
- A: Las Chutney
- B: Las Tartare
- C: Las Ketchup
- D: Las Mustard

You have won at least £1,000!

6) £2,000
In basketball, what is the name of the board to which the hoop is attached?
- A: Headboard
- B: Backboard
- C: Flatboard
- D: Springboard

7) £4,000
Which of these is a type of shark?
- A: Matron
- B: Doctor
- C: Nurse
- D: Surgeon

8) £8,000
What colour is the cross on the Finnish national flag?
- A: Blue
- B: Red
- C: Yellow
- D: White

9) £16,000
What does an horologist make?
- A: Furniture
- B: Maps
- C: Telescopes
- D: Clocks

10) £32,000
Where is there an elected body called the House of Keys?
- A: Sark
- B: Jersey
- C: Isle of Man
- D: Alderney

You have won at least £32,000!

11) £64,000
Which of these is a book in the New Testament?
- A: Jeremiah
- B: Job
- C: Jonah
- D: Jude

12) £125,000
What is usually the main ingredient of the German dish sauerbraten?
- A: Bread
- B: Cabbage
- C: Beef
- D: Sausage

13) £250,000
Which of the following is England's highest peak?
- A: Skiddaw
- B: Scafell Pike
- C: Helvellyn
- D: Cross Fell

14) £500,000
Who was the Roman goddess of the hearth?
- A: Isis
- B: Cybele
- C: Juno
- D: Vesta

15) £1,000,000
Near the mouth of which river is the city of Londonderry situated?
- A: Liffey
- B: Bann
- C: Foyle
- D: Erne

GAME 29 ANSWERS PAGE 62

50:50 from page 52

Ask The Audience from page 56

Phone-A-Friend

CONGRATULATIONS YOU ARE A MILLIONAIRE!

1) £100

What is the offspring of a donkey and a horse called?

- A: Slipper
- B: Boot
- C: Mule
- D: Sandal

2) £200

What was the name of King Arthur's wife?

- A: Guinevere
- B: Godiva
- C: Maid Marian
- D: Anne Boleyn

3) £300

Which slogan was most associated with the Spice Girls?

- A: Bad Girls
- B: Girl Power
- C: Lucky Girls
- D: Girls Forever

4) £500

The ballet solo made famous by Anna Pavlova is 'The Dying ...'?

- A: Flamingo
- B: Robin
- C: Pigeon
- D: Swan

5) £1,000

What is the title of the Corr's first UK No 1 single, which reached the top spot in July 2000?

- A: Winded
- B: Gasping
- C: Panting
- D: Breathless

You have won at least £1,000!

6) £2,000

Apart from his yellow spots, what colour was the TV character Mr Blobby?

- A: Green
- B: Black
- C: Pink
- D: Blue

7) £4,000

Baton Rouge is the capital of which US state?

- A: Montana
- B: North Carolina
- C: Wisconsin
- D: Louisiana

8) £8,000

What is the world's largest living marsupial?

- A: Red kangaroo
- B: Water opossum
- C: Common wombat
- D: Scrub wallaby

9) £16,000

Which of these US cities stands on the shores of the Great Lakes?

- A: Baltimore
- B: Chicago
- C: Kansas City
- D: Cincinnati

10) £32,000

Which of these acids is used in baking powder?

- A: Acetic acid
- B: Malic acid
- C: Lactic acid
- D: Tartaric acid

You have won at least £32,000!

11) £64,000

Which country won the Jules Rimet Trophy outright in 1970?

- A: USA
- B: Brazil
- C: Australia
- D: Japan

12) £125,000

Which country's parliament consists of the Rajya Sabha and the Lok Sabha?

- A: Malaysia
- B: India
- C: Pakistan
- D: Guyana

13) £250,000

In the 16th century, what was a dandiprat?

- A: Small coin
- B: Gallon of ale
- C: River boat
- D: Foppish man

14) £500,000

Which is Britain's oldest recorded town?

- A: St Albans
- B: Canterbury
- C: Colchester
- D: Bath

15) £1,000,000

A buckling is what type of smoked fish?

- A: Mackerel
- B: Herring
- C: Salmon
- D: Trout

GAME 30 ANSWERS PAGE 62

50:50 from page 52

Ask The Audience from page 56

Phone-A-Friend

CONGRATULATIONS YOU ARE A MILLIONAIRE!

GAME 31

1) £100
Which part of a bird is also a slang term for a judge?
- A: Feather
- B: Beak
- C: Claw
- D: Wing

2) £200
According to legend, what were chased out of Ireland by St Patrick?
- A: The Corrs
- B: Snakes
- C: Nuns
- D: Builders

3) £300
In March 2002, Yoko Ono unveiled a statue of which Beatle at Liverpool airport?
- A: Ringo
- B: John
- C: Paul
- D: George

4) £500
Which of these is a dance similar to the samba?
- A: Super nova
- B: Bossa nova
- C: Casa nova
- D: Terra nova

5) £1000
In industry, what is the opposite of nationalisation?
- A: Privatisation
- B: Publication
- C: Accreditation
- D: Pasteurisation

You have won at least £1000!

6) £2000
Which ingredient gives mead its sweet taste?
- A: Sugar cane
- B: Honey
- C: Maple syrup
- D: Apple juice

7) £4000
Which ballet term is derived from the French for 'spinning top'?
- A: Pirouette
- B: Entrechat
- C: Jeté
- D: Arabesque

8) £8,000
What does the 'E' stand for in the acronym Epcot?
- A: European
- B: Early
- C: Experimental
- D: Energy

9) £16,000
A passerine bird is one adapted for what?
- A: Wading
- B: Perching
- C: Hovering
- D: Night flight

10) £32,000
In which British city is Strangeways prison?
- A: Manchester
- B: Liverpool
- C: Newcastle
- D: Leeds

You have won at least £32,000!

11) £64,000
Which of these is a small songbird with a noisy cry?
- A: Prattler
- B: Gabbler
- C: Babbler
- D: Jabberer

12) £125,000
In which range of hills did the Border terrier originate?
- A: Pennines
- B: Cotswolds
- C: Cheviots
- D: Malvern

13) £250,000
Which of the following is a plant?
- A: Fat Hen
- B: Obese Duck
- C: Chubby Swan
- D: Plump Gull

14) £500,000
Which English monarch had the shortest reign - just two and a half months?
- A: Edward VI
- B: Edward II
- C: Edward VIII
- D: Edward V

15) £1,000,000
Which duke holds the title Earl Marshal?
- A: Norfolk
- B: Bedford
- C: Marlborough
- D: Westminister

GAME 31 ANSWERS PAGE 63

50:50 from page 52
Ask The Audience from page 56
Phone-A-Friend

CONGRATULATIONS YOU ARE A MILLIONAIRE!

GAME 32

1) £100
Which bird is a common summer visitor to Britain?
- A: Gulp
- B: Quaff
- C: Swallow
- D: Sip

2) £200
In classical mythology, what was the drink of the Gods?
- A: Nectar
- B: Coca-cola
- C: Light ale
- D: Gin & tonic

3) £300
Which rock star and campaigner was the lead singer with The Boomtown Rats?
- A: Midge Ure
- B: Sting
- C: Bono
- D: Bob Geldof

4) £500
Which pop star adopted a symbol in place of his name in 1993?
- A: Prince
- B: Boy George
- C: Sting
- D: Elton John

5) £1,000
Which of these Kennedys is not a member of the US political dynasty?
- A: John
- B: Nigel
- C: Robert
- D: Edward

You have won at least £1,000!

6) £2,000
In which city is the TV sitcom 'The Royle Family' set?
- A: Manchester
- B: London
- C: Birmingham
- D: Liverpool

7) £4,000
Glyndebourne is most famous for what kind of festival?
- A: Film
- B: Food
- C: Vintage cars
- D: Opera

8) £8,000
The word ternary refers to which number?
- A: Two
- B: Three
- C: Four
- D: Five

9) £16,000
Which cartoonist is best known for his drawings of overweight ponies?
- A: Trogg
- B: Scarfe
- C: Thelwell
- D: Giles

10) £32,000
Carrots are a particularly good source of which vitamin?
- A: Vitamin A
- B: Vitamin D
- C: Vitamin E
- D: Vitamin K

You have won at least £32,000!

11) £64,000
With whom did David Bowie team up to record 'Dancing In The Streets' in 1985?
- A: Bono
- B: Van Morrison
- C: Debbie Harry
- D: Mick Jagger

12) £125,000
Who is the eldest brother in the McGann acting family?
- A: Paul
- B: Joe
- C: Mark
- D: Stephen

13) £250,000
Which official represents the Crown in a British colony?
- A: Chief Minister
- B: Sheriff
- C: Governor
- D: Equerry

14) £500,000
Nassau, the capital of the Bahamas, is on which island?
- A: New Providence
- B: Andros
- C: Grand Bahama
- D: Abaco

15) £1,000,000
Which was the last battleship to serve with the Royal Navy?
- A: HMS Valiant
- B: HMS Vigilant
- C: HMS Vengeance
- D: HMS Vanguard

GAME 32
ANSWERS
PAGE 63

50:50
from page 52
Ask The Audience
from page 56
Phone-A-Friend

CONGRATULATIONS YOU ARE A MILLIONAIRE!

33

GAME 33

1) £100

Which of these might live in a hive?

- A: Bees
- B: Birds
- C: Ants
- D: Chickens

2) £200

According to the title of a waltz by Strauss, what colour is the Danube?

- A: Green
- B: Black
- C: Blue
- D: Pink

3) £300

Who had a huge UK hit with 'You Sexy Thing' in 1975, and again in 1997?

- A: Milk Shake
- B: Mint Tea
- C: Hot Chocolate
- D: Black Coffee

4) £500

According to the title of the hit song, what is tied 'round the old oak tree'?

- A: Blue shoelace
- B: Red dickie bow
- C: Yellow ribbon
- D: Green hanky

5) £1,000

Which device in a computer makes it possible to access the Internet?

- A: Modem
- B: Boot
- C: Mouse
- D: Floppy disk

You have won at least £1,000!

6) £2,000

What kind of creature is a pipistrelle?

- A: Bat
- B: Mouse
- C: Butterfly
- D: Cat

7) £4,000

What is the first name of Russia's President Putin?

- A: Boris
- B: Vladimir
- C: Mikhail
- D: Leonid

8) £8,000

Pseuds Corner is a feature of which magazine?

- A: Cosmopolitan
- B: Private Eye
- C: The Economist
- D: The Spectator

9) £16,000

Which of the following is a legal writ?

- A: Stabat mater
- B: Ipso facto
- C: Habeas corpus
- D: Caveat emptor

10) £32,000

In which city was Florence Nightingale born?

- A: Naples
- B: Rome
- C: Venice
- D: Florence

You have won at least £32,000!

11) £64,000

What would interest a 'gricer'?

- A: Birds
- B: Railways
- C: Shop signs
- D: Post cards

12) £125,000

Which Scottish castle is the setting for Shakespeare's 'Macbeth'?

- A: Stirling
- B: Blair
- C: Cawdor
- D: Glamis

13) £250,000

Which building houses the Irish National Parliament?

- A: Munster House
- B: Leinster House
- C: Connacht House
- D: Ulster House

14) £500,000

Which sport would interest a toxophilite?

- A: Archery
- B: Skeet Shooting
- C: Diving
- D: Orienteering

15) £1,000,000

An eyas is a young what?

- A: Eagle
- B: Owl
- C: Hawk
- D: Penguin

GAME 33 ANSWERS PAGE 62

50:50 from page 52

Ask The Audience from page 56

Phone-A-Friend

CONGRATULATIONS YOU ARE A MILLIONAIRE!

GAME 34

1) £100
In Greek mythology, a centaur was half man and half what?

- A: Horse
- B: Hedgehog
- C: Hippopotamus
- D: Hamster

2) £200
What type of unplanned session might be given by pop musicians?

- A: Marmalade
- B: Jam
- C: Honey
- D: Marmite

3) £300
Complete the name of the rock band, Velvet ...?

- A: Line
- B: Metro
- C: Underground
- D: Subway

4) £500
Which of these was a hit single for Simon and Garfunkel?

- A: Mrs Henderson
- B: Mrs Stevenson
- C: Mrs Hutchinson
- D: Mrs Robinson

5) £1,000
Which of these has the smallest numerical answer?

- A: 3 + 3
- B: 3 x 3
- C: 3 – 3
- D: 3 ≥

You have won at least £1,000!

6) £2,000
What was Sri Lanka previously called?

- A: Gibraltar
- B: Ceylon
- C: Madagascar
- D: Madeira

7) £4,000
Who succeeded Henry VIII to the English throne?

- A: Elizabeth I
- B: Edward VI
- C: Mary I
- D: James I

8) £8,000
Maria Shriver, wife of Arnold Schwarzenegger, is the niece of which former US president?

- A: Jimmy Carter
- B: Richard Nixon
- C: John F Kennedy
- D: Gerald Ford

9) £16,000
Which Shakespearean character becomes Thane of Cawdor?

- A: Banquo
- B: Macbeth
- C: Macduff
- D: Donalbain

10) £32,000
Sir Michael Stoute is a famous name in which sport?

- A: Tennis
- B: Motor racing
- C: Golf
- D: Horse racing

You have won at least £32,000!

11) £64,000
Who wrote the novel 'Middlemarch'?

- A: George Eliot
- B: Mrs Gaskell
- C: Jane Austen
- D: Emily Brontë

12) £125,000
Which UK coin bears the inscription 'Standing on the Shoulders of Giants'?

- A: £1
- B: £2
- C: 10p
- D: 50p

13) £250,000
In which sport is there an official called the Lady Paramount?

- A: Croquet
- B: Archery
- C: Golf
- D: Bowls

14) £500,000
Which Italian city hosted the 2006 Winter Olympic Games?

- A: Milan
- B: Turin
- C: Palermo
- D: Venice

15) £1,000,000
What is the capital city of Slovenia?

- A: Skopje
- B: Split
- C: Ljubljana
- D: Zagreb

GAME 34 ANSWERS PAGE 63

50:50 from page 52
Ask The Audience from page 56
Phone-A-Friend

CONGRATULATIONS YOU ARE A MILLIONAIRE!

1) £100

If you are unable to recognise a person, you do not know him from who?

- A: Aaron
- B: Andrew
- C: Abraham
- D: Adam

2) £200

Complete the name of the pop group, ... South?

- A: Pretty
- B: Fair
- C: Picturesque
- D: Beautiful

3) £300

The age of a tree can generally be determined by counting its what?

- A: Leaves
- B: Birds' nests
- C: Rings
- D: Acorns

4) £500

Complete the title of the Chuck Berry song, 'Roll Over ...'?

- A: Mozart
- B: Beethoven
- C: Handel
- D: Tchaikovsky

5) £1,000

In physics, what does the abbreviation UV stand for?

- A: Ultravariable
- B: Ultravisual
- C: Ultraviolet
- D: Ultravector

You have won at least £1,000!

6) £2,000

Whom did Jennifer Aniston play in the US sitcom 'Friends'?

- A: Rachel
- B: Susan
- C: Phoebe
- D: Monica

7) £4,000

How many is ten to the power of three?

- A: 100
- B: 1,000
- C: 10,000
- D: 100,000

8) £8,000

What nationality are the singing twins, the Cheeky Girls?

- A: Romanian
- B: German
- C: Turkish
- D: Bulgarian

9) £16,000

In Germany, what kind of building is a schloss?

- A: Church
- B: Castle
- C: Sports centre
- D: Town hall

10) £32,000

What is a naevus?

- A: Navel
- B: Birthmark
- C: Hiccup
- D: Adam's apple

You have won at least £32,000!

11) £64,000

Who were Johnny Kidd's backing group?

- A: Corsairs
- B: Pirates
- C: Buccaneers
- D: Jolly Rogers

12) £125,000

Who is the Roman equivalent to the Greek goddess Athena?

- A: Venus
- B: Victoria
- C: Minerva
- D: Diana

13) £250,000

Which is the most abundant element in the Earth's crust?

- A: Silicon
- B: Aluminium
- C: Iron
- D: Oxygen

14) £500,000

Who wrote the original book 'The One Hundred and One Dalmatians'?

- A: Frank Baum
- B: P L Travers
- C: Enid Blyton
- D: Dodie Smith

15) £1,000,000

The oldest existing suspension bridge in the UK spans which river?

- A: Severn
- B: Tweed
- C: Humber
- D: Thames

CONGRATULATIONS YOU ARE A MILLIONAIRE!

GAME 34 ANSWERS PAGE 63

50:50 from page 52

Ask The Audience from page 56

Phone-A-Friend

GAME 36

1) £100
Which of these are particularly associated with Scotland?
- A: Panpipes
- B: Blowpipes
- C: Drainpipes
- D: Bagpipes

2) £200
Which boy band's original line-up was Gary, Howard, Jason, Mark and Robbie?
- A: That's That
- B: How's That?
- C: Take That
- D: Just Like That

3) £300
Which of these is the name of a plant?
- A: Wolfscarf
- B: Foxglove
- C: Squirrelhat
- D: Rabbitsocks

4) £500
What does a thermostat normally regulate?
- A: Light
- B: Water
- C: Temperature
- D: Pressure

5) £1,000
What type of drug is penicillin?
- A: Antibiotic
- B: Antacid
- C: Antihistamine
- D: Analgesic

You have won at least £1,000!

6) £2,000
In 'The X-Files', what is agent Scully's first name?
- A: Debbie
- B: Diana
- C: Daphne
- D: Dana

7) £4,000
Who received a $7 million Picasso painting in lieu of earnings for the film 'Aladdin'?
- A: Tom Hanks
- B: Robin Williams
- C: Tim Allen
- D: Billy Crystal

8) £8,000
Which flower takes its name from the Latin word for a wolf?
- A: Delphinium
- B: Hollyhock
- C: Lupin
- D: Lobelia

9) £16,000
The name of which card game is derived from the Spanish word for 'basket'?
- A: Pontoon
- B: Baccarat
- C: Poker
- D: Canasta

10) £32,000
In which country is the Apennine mountain range?
- A: France
- B: Spain
- C: Switzerland
- D: Italy

You have won at least £32,000!

11) £64,000
Which of the following coniferous trees is deciduous?
- A: Cedar
- B: Larch
- C: Cypress
- D: Yew

12) £125,000
Which of the following was not one of the ten plagues of Egypt?
- A: Locusts
- B: Rats
- C: Frogs
- D: Boils

13) £250,000
Which airline uses the designator code KM?
- A: KLM
- B: Air Mauritius
- C: Air Malta
- D: Kenya Airways

14) £500,000
Which vitamin is necessary for the proper clotting of blood?
- A: B
- B: D
- C: K
- D: C

15) £1,000,000
Which was Abba's second UK No 1 single?
- A: Waterloo
- B: Fernando
- C: Dancing Queen
- D: Mamma Mia

GAME 36 ANSWERS PAGE 63

50:50 from page 52
Ask The Audience from page 56
Phone-A-Friend

CONGRATULATIONS YOU ARE A MILLIONAIRE!

GAME 37

1) £100
Which of these is a type of vegetable?
- A: Jumper bean
- B: Runner bean
- C: Hurdler bean
- D: Leaper bean

2) £200
What colour submarine was the title of a hit single for The Beatles?
- A: Purple
- B: Yellow
- C: Orange
- D: Pink

3) £300
By what abbreviation of her forename was Margaret Thatcher popularly known?
- A: Meg
- B: Peggy
- C: Maggie
- D: Marge

4) £500
To which constituent of the body does the rhesus factor relate?
- A: Bone
- B: Skin
- C: Muscle
- D: Blood

5) £1,000
For which country does Ronaldo play internation football?
- A: Italy
- B: France
- C: Argentina
- D: Brazil

You have won at least £1,000!

6) £2,000
Where do the Teletubbies live?
- A: Home Hill
- B: Green Hill
- C: High Hill
- D: Dinky Dell

7) £4,000
Which ex- 'EastEnder' starred in 'Ultimate Force'?
- A: Ross Kemp
- B: Todd Carty
- C: Susan Tully
- D: Anita Dobson

8) £8,000
Which of these Shakespearean characters kills his wife?
- A: Hamlet
- B: King Lear
- C: Othello
- D: Julius Caesar

9) £16,000
In the title of the novel by Gabriel García Márquez, how many 'Years of Solitude' are there?
- A: One Thousand
- B: Fifty
- C: Two Hundred
- D: One Hundred

10) £32,000
Which of these is a large species of beetle?
- A: Goliath
- B: Hercules
- C: Samson
- D: Atlas

You have won at least £32,000!

11) £64,000
To which of these senses does the adjective olfactory relate?
- A: Sight
- B: Touch
- C: Smell
- D: Taste

12) £125,000
What would you expect to find in a book called a grimoire?
- A: Prayers
- B: Recipes
- C: Spells
- D: Songs

13) £250,000
Who is the Greek equivalent of the Roman god Ceres?
- A: Dionysus
- B: Demeter
- C: Pan
- D: Hermes

14) £500,000
In electronics, which of these is not part of a transistor?
- A: Fuse
- B: Base
- C: Emitter
- D: Collector

15) £1,000,000
What kind of creature is the Nova Scotia Duck?
- A: Bird
- B: Cat
- C: Sheep
- D: Dog

CONGRATULATIONS YOU ARE A MILLIONAIRE!

GAME 37 ANSWERS PAGE 63

50:50 from page 52

Ask The Audience from page 56

Phone-A-Friend

1) £100
Which of the following is a common wild flower?
- A: Margedish
- B: Buttercup
- C: Florabowl
- D: Spreadplate

2) £200
Complete the title of the hit single for Queen, 'Radio ...'?
- A: Ra Ra
- B: La La
- C: Ga Ga
- D: Na Na

3) £300
A student would normally use a Bunsen burner in which lesson?
- A: History
- B: French
- C: PE
- D: Chemistry

4) £500
Edgbaston and Trent Bridge are famous venues for which sport?
- A: Football
- B: Polo
- C: Cricket
- D: Hockey

5) £1,000
Which of these is the name for an official at motor racing events?
- A: Marshal
- B: Sheriff
- C: Commodore
- D: Alderman

You have won at least £1,000!

6) £2,000
Which character is voiced by Cameron Diaz in the 2001 animated comedy 'Shrek'?
- A: Queen Emma
- B: Princess Fiona
- C: Countess Anna
- D: Duchess Eva

7) £4,000
Dennis Waterman played which actor's minder in the TV series of the same name?
- A: George Cole
- B: John Thaw
- C: David Jason
- D: Bob Hoskins

8) £8,000
Which of these is a traditional name for a clown?
- A: Jacky
- B: Joey
- C: Johnny
- D: Jimmy

9) £16,000
Elizabeth David is best known as a writer on what subject?
- A: Gardening
- B: Cookery
- C: Fashion
- D: Needlework

10) £32,000
John Bonham was the drummer with which rock band?
- A: Pink Floyd
- B: Led Zeppelin
- C: Cream
- D: The Who

You have won at least £32,000!

11) £64,000
Which of these is not a model of vehicle made by Ford?
- A: Mustang
- B: Palomino
- C: Maverick
- D: Pinto

12) £125,000
What is a hygrometer used to measure?
- A: Density
- B: Humidity
- C: Heat
- D: Height

13) £250,000
In which country has the highest ever temperature, 58°C, been recorded?
- A: USA
- B: Libya
- C: Algeria
- D: Iraq

14) £500,000
Which of the following is not a giant?
- A: Despair
- B: Cyclops
- C: Magog
- D: Sleipnir

15) £1,000,000
During the English Civil War, what were the royalists called by their opponents?
- A: Hooligans
- B: Delinquents
- C: Riff-raff
- D: Blackguards

GAME 38 ANSWERS PAGE 63

50:50 from page 52
Ask The Audience from page 56
Phone-A-Friend

CONGRATULATIONS YOU ARE A MILLIONAIRE!

1) £100
Which animal is tradionally regarded as a beast of burden?
- A: Monkey
- B: Lion
- C: Donkey
- D: Giraffe

2) £200
What colour were the 'Suede Shoes' Elvis Presley sang about?
- A: Red
- B: Blue
- C: Green
- D: Shocking pink

3) £300
'Gnashers' is an informal term for which parts of the body?
- A: Eyeballs
- B: Teeth
- C: Fingernails
- D: Kneecaps

4) £500
In which sport might a googly or a yorker be encountered?
- A: Table tennis
- B: Cricket
- C: Golf
- D: Hockey

5) £1,000
The final of the 2003 Rugby World Cup took place in which city?
- A: Sydney
- B: Adelaide
- C: Canberra
- D: Brisbane

You have won at least £1,000!

6) £2,000
Which Irish-born actor received an honorary OBE in July 2003?
- A: Colm Meaney
- B: Pierce Brosnan
- C: Gabriel Bryne
- D: Niall Toibin

7) £4,000
Which 1980s pop group included George Michael and Andrew Ridgeley?
- A: Wham!
- B: The Police
- C: Duran Duran
- D: Culture Club

8) £8,000
Which England rugby union star is the nephew of a 1966 football World Cup winner?
- A: Mike Catt
- B: Phil Vickery
- C: Ben Cohen
- D: Dan Luger

9) £16,000
How is Schubert's Symphony No 8 also known?
- A: New World
- B: Unfinished
- C: Trout
- D: Pathétique

10) £32,000
Which British monarch was the last of the Hanoverians?
- A: Edward VII
- B: William IV
- C: Victoria
- D: George IV

You have won at least £32,000!

11) £64,000
Which rock legend was born on 8th January 1935?
- A: Cliff Richard
- B: Bill Haley
- C: Ringo Starr
- D: Elvis Presley

12) £125,000
Sally Ride was the first female American what?
- A: Senator
- B: Astronaut
- C: Fighter pilot
- D: Bishop

13) £250,000
Which river did Capability Brown divert to flow past Chatsworth House?
- A: Trent
- B: Dove
- C: Derwent
- D: Ouse

14) £500,000
Where on the human body might Beau's Lines appear?
- A: Eyelids
- B: Knees
- C: Fingernails
- D: Palms

15) £1,000,000
In golf, which modern club is equivalent to the club known as the 'spoon'?
- A: Pitching wedge
- B: No 3 wood
- C: No 9 iron
- D: Sand wedge

GAME 39 ANSWERS PAGE 63

50:50 from page 52
Ask The Audience from page 56
Phone-A-Friend

CONGRATULATIONS YOU ARE A MILLIONAIRE!

GAME 40

1) £100
How are very muscular men sometimes referred to?
- A: Lambcake
- B: Porkcake
- C: Beefcake
- D: Muttoncake

2) £200
Of which 1980s pop duo was Marc Almond the lead singer?
- A: Tough Cell
- B: Soft Cell
- C: Mushy Cell
- D: Hard Cell

3) £300
Which cricketing body was founded in London in 1787?
- A: MMC
- B: MCM
- C: CCM
- D: MCC

4) £500
What nationality is the footballer Ryan Giggs?
- A: Scottish
- B: Dutch
- C: Welsh
- D: French

5) £1,000
Which award-winning TV series features the Fishers, a family of undertakers?
- A: The Sopranos
- B: Seinfeld
- C: Ally McBeal
- D: Six Feet Under

You have won at least £1,000!

6) £2,000
In 1990, 'Fog on the Tyne' was a hit single for Lindisfarne and which footballer?
- A: Paul Gascoigne
- B: Gary Lineker
- C: John Barnes
- D: Chris Waddle

7) £4,000
Who features on David Bowie's single 'Space Oddity'?
- A: Captain Kirk
- B: General Rule
- C: Colonel Blimp
- D: Major Tom

8) £8,000
A 'tournedos Rossini' is a steak topped with which of these ingredients?
- A: Spinach
- B: Smoked salmon
- C: Truffles
- D: Foie gras

9) £16,000
In musical notation, which of these is the longest note?
- A: Quaver
- B: Crotchet
- C: Minim
- D: Semibreve

10) £32,000
For whom did Shah Jahan build the Taj Mahal as a mausoleum?
- A: His mother
- B: His son
- C: His daughter
- D: His wife

You have won at least £32,000!

11) £64,000
Which of these started life as the Anglo-Persian Oil Company?
- A: Shell
- B: Mobil
- C: Esso
- D: BP

12) £125,000
Which of these cities does not have a passport office?
- A: Glasgow
- B: Birmingham
- C: Belfast
- D: Liverpool

13) £250,000
The dinar is the standard unit of currency in which of these countries?
- A: Syria
- B: Jordan
- C: Saudi Arabia
- D: Eritrea

14) £500,000
Axilla is the anatomical name for which part of the human body?
- A: Hip
- B: Armpit
- C: Heel bone
- D: Big toe

15) £1,000,000
What is the actor Rob Lowe's middle name?
- A: Assistant
- B: Helper
- C: Aider
- D: Backer

CONGRATULATIONS YOU ARE A MILLIONAIRE!

GAME 40 ANSWERS PAGE 63

50:50 from page 52
Ask The Audience from page 56
Phone-A-Friend

41

GAME 41

1) £100
Which is a nurse who runs a hospital ward?
- A: Levy nurse
- B: Cost nurse
- C: Debit nurse
- D: Charge nurse

2) £200
What is the title of Chris De Burgh's most successful single?
- A: Lady In White
- B: Lady In Red
- C: Lady In Black
- D: Lady In Cerise

3) £300
In relation to sports fixtures, what is the opposite of 'home'?
- A: Along
- B: Away
- C: Afar
- D: Astray

4) £500
Which of the following is a method of scoring in American football?
- A: Setdown
- B: Touchdown
- C: Putdown
- D: Fall down

5) £1,000
Who won 'I'm A Celebrity ... Get Me Out Of Here' in December 2004?
- A: Paul Burrell
- B: Vic Reeves
- C: Joe Pasquale
- D: Fran Cosgrave

You have won at least £1,000!

6) £2,000
The Bundesbank is the central bank of which country?
- A: Denmark
- B: Belgium
- C: Germany
- D: Czech Republic

7) £4,000
Which of these is a type of bird?
- A: Corncrake
- B: Cornucopia
- C: Corniche
- D: Cornea

8) £8,000
On which racecourse is the St Leger run?
- A: Epsom
- B: Newmarket
- C: Aintree
- D: Doncaster

9) £16,000
What relation was Queen Anne to Queen Mary II?
- A: Cousin
- B: Sister
- C: Daughter
- D: Granddaughter

10) £32,000
What is the title of Luxembourg's head of state?
- A: Crown Prince
- B: King
- C: Grand Duke
- D: Emperor

You have won at least £32,000!

11) £64,000
In the video game, who dreams of becoming a great Pokémon trainer?
- A: Oak
- B: Elm
- C: Ash
- D: Willow

12) £125,000
Tashkent is the capital city of which country?
- A: Ukraine
- B: Georgia
- C: Uzbekistan
- D: Azerbaijan

13) £250,000
What nationality is the UN Secretary-General Kofi Annan?
- A: Ugandan
- B: Ghanaian
- C: Kenyan
- D: Nigerian

14) £500,000
Melomania is a craze for what?
- A: Power
- B: Suntan
- C: Music
- D: Drama

15) £1,000,000
What is the name of the magazine edited by Danny Devito's character in 'LA Confidential'?
- A: On the QT
- B: Scandal!
- C: Hush Hush
- D: Sssshh!

GAME 41 ANSWERS PAGE 63

50:50 from page 52
Ask The Audience from page 56
Phone-A-Friend

CONGRATULATIONS YOU ARE A MILLIONAIRE!

GAME 42

1) £100
Which of these is used in conjunction with a computer?
- A: Sloppy disk
- B: Flappy disk
- C: Slappy disk
- D: Floppy disk

2) £200
Which two letters indicate that someone is a Member of Parliament at Westminister?
- A: MC
- B: MH
- C: MP
- D: MD

3) £300
Where was the TV sitcom 'Hi De Hi!' set?
- A: Prison
- B: Stately home
- C: Post office
- D: Holiday camp

4) £500
Which of these is a shot in tennis?
- A: Backhand
- B: Backslide
- C: Backstop
- D: Backlash

5) £1,000
What is the first name of the main character in the sitcom 'Keeping Up Appearances'?
- A: Honeysuckle
- B: Hydrangea
- C: Hollyhock
- D: Hyacinth

You have won at least £1,000!

6) £2,000
The young of which of these birds are called ducklings?
- A: Plover
- B: Coot
- C: Moorhen
- D: Mallard

7) £4,000
Which specific bones of the body form the thoracic cage?
- A: Knuckles
- B: Vertebrae
- C: Ribs
- D: Tarsals

8) £8,000
To which bodily process does the word peptic relate?
- A: Breathing
- B: Hearing
- C: Digestion
- D: Pulse rate

9) £16,000
What nationality is the Formula 1 racing driver Kimi Raikkonen?
- A: Finnish
- B: Belgian
- C: Brazilian
- D: Dutch

10) £32,000
In which of these athletics events may a competitor wear a glove?
- A: Hammer
- B: Discus
- C: Javelin
- D: Shot put

You have won at least £32,000!

11) £64,000
At which English racecourse is the One Thousand Guineas usually run?
- A: Newmarket
- B: Epsom
- C: Doncaster
- D: Lingfield

12) £125,000
In Greek mythology, who helped Theseus escape from Labyrinth?
- A: Andromeda
- B: Ariadne
- C: Athene
- D: Artemis

13) £250,000
Sercial is a variety of which fortified wine?
- A: Sherry
- B: Port
- C: Madeira
- D: Marsala

14) £500,000
In which film did Greta Garbo speak the famous line, 'I want to be alone'?
- A: Mata Hari
- B: Anna Karenina
- C: Grand Hotel
- D: Anna Christie

15) £1,000,000
Which English county was historically divided into rapes?
- A: Yorkshire
- B: Kent
- C: Sussex
- D: Surrey

GAME 42 ANSWERS PAGE 63

50:50 from page 52
Ask The Audience from page 56
Phone-A-Friend

CONGRATULATIONS YOU ARE A MILLIONAIRE!

GAME 43

1) £100
Complete the name of the legendary singer, Roy ...?
- A: Spherison
- B: Globison
- C: Orbison
- D: Ballison

2) £200
What is the most popular name for a silicon chip or integrated circuit?
- A: Microspud
- B: Microcrisp
- C: Microchip
- D: Microtatty

3) £300
What type of shoes gave the title of a TV drama starring Jimmy Nail as a budding singer?
- A: Alligator
- B: Cayman
- C: Lizard
- D: Crocodile

4) £500
Which of these applies to the cartoon character Mr Magoo?
- A: No teeth
- B: Deaf
- C: Short-sighted
- D: Dyslexic

5) £1,000
Watford Gap is a service station on which motorway?
- A: M1
- B: M2
- C: M3
- D: M4

You have won at least £1,000!

6) £2,000
What does English Heritage use to mark the homes of famous people in London?
- A: Green doors
- B: Red stars
- C: Blue plaques
- D: Gold doorsteps

7) £4,000
With which of these sports is Donington Park associated?
- A: Polo
- B: Water skiing
- C: Motor racing
- D: Athletics

8) £8,000
Which school was attended by Prince Philip and his three sons?
- A: Harrow
- B: Rugby
- C: Gordonstoun
- D: Eton

9) £16,000
In which TV series did Woody Harrelson play Woody Boyd the barman?
- A: Friends
- B: Taxi
- C: Cheers
- D: Roseanne

10) £32,000
Which of these is a position in rugby union but not in rugby league?
- A: Hooker
- B: Winger
- C: Flanker
- D: Scrum half

You have won at least £32,000!

11) £64,000
Which of these is a pass in American football?
- A: Zip fastener
- B: Hook & eye
- C: Buttonhook
- D: Toggle & loop

12) £125,000
Which month of the Muslim year is Ramadan?
- A: First
- B: Third
- C: Sixth
- D: Ninth

13) £250,000
As used on the Internet, what does the 'M' stand for in the abbreviation HTML?
- A: Multilayer
- B: Markup
- C: Megabyte
- D: Machine

14) £500,000
What is a 'kit-cat'?
- A: Chocolate bar
- B: Sports bag
- C: Kitten
- D: Portrait

15) £1,000,000
Near which lake did William and Dorothy Wordsworth live from 1799?
- A: Derwentwater
- B: Ullswater
- C: Grasmere
- D: Windermere

GAME 43 ANSWERS PAGE 64

50:50 from page 52
Ask The Audience from page 56
Phone-A-Friend

CONGRATULATIONS YOU ARE A MILLIONAIRE!

44

GAME 44

1) £100
Which of these colours does not appear on the Union Jack?
- A: Red
- B: Green
- C: White
- D: Blue

2) £200
Which boy's name is also a miners' safety lamp?
- A: Johnny
- B: Davy
- C: Gary
- D: Larry

3) £300
Which character is played by Leonard Nimoy in the TV series 'Star Trek'?
- A: Mr Spock
- B: Mr Crock
- C: Mr Spook
- D: Mr Crook

4) £500
Who are Fred Flintstone's neighbours?
- A: The Rubbles
- B: The Screes
- C: The Bits
- D: The Clinkers

5) £1,000
Which of these insects shares its name with a British WWII aircraft?
- A: Beetle
- B: Locust
- C: Mosquito
- D: Greenfly

You have won at least £1,000!

6) £2,000
A vicereine is the wife of the holder of which title?
- A: Vice-chairman
- B: Viceroy
- C: Vice-president
- D: Vice admiral

7) £4,000
What number follows Daytona and Indianapolis in the names of the two famous motor races?
- A: 5000
- B: 200
- C: 3000
- D: 500

8) £8,000
What family name do the aliens adopt in the TV comedy '3rd Rock from the Sun'?
- A: Solomon
- B: Johnson
- C: Dubeck
- D: Williams

9) £16,000
Which colour card is issued to a hockey player as a warning for foul play?
- A: Green
- B: Red
- C: Yellow
- D: White

10) £32,000
In which sport is 'stableford' a system of awarding points?
- A: Horse racing
- B: Table tennis
- C: Golf
- D: Polo

You have won at least £32,000!

11) £64,000
For which mammal is Vulpes vulpes the zoological name?
- A: Badger
- B: Fox
- C: Otter
- D: Weasel

12) £125,000
Which amendment to the US Constitution guarantees the right to trial by jury?
- A: Second
- B: Fourth
- C: Fifth
- D: Seventh

13) £250,000
'Goodbye to All That' is the autobiography of which British writer?
- A: T S Eliot
- B: Robert Graves
- C: Philip Larkin
- D: Ted Hughes

14) £500,000
Who swam nightly across the Hellespont to visit Hero?
- A: Lysander
- B: Demetrius
- C: Leander
- D: Endymion

15) £1,000,000
Where could you visit Fingal's Cave?
- A: Inner Hebrides
- B: Isle of Sky
- C: Isle of Jura
- D: Outer Hebrides

GAME 44 ANSWERS PAGE 64

50:50
from page 52
**Ask The Audience
from page 56**
Phone-A-Friend

CONGRATULATIONS YOU ARE A MILLIONAIRE!

GAME 45

1) £100
In which English county are the Norfolk Broads?
- A: Essex
- B: Somerset
- C: Surrey
- D: Norfolk

2) £200
A 'pop-up' is a type of which domestic appliance?
- A: Kettle
- B: Toaster
- C: Microwave
- D: Fridge

3) £300
In the sitcom of the same name, what sort of establishment was 'Fawlty Towers'?
- A: Garage
- B: Hotel
- C: Leisure centre
- D: Builder's yard

4) £500
What is a TV programme called which is made up of assorted features?
- A: Newspaper
- B: Journal
- C: Magazine
- D: Comic

5) £1000
Which of these airports is in Scotland?
- A: Prestwick
- B: Gatwick
- C: Stansted
- D: Lydd

You have won at least £1000!

6) £2000
Which band had a UK No 1 single in 2004 with 'Obviously'?
- A: McCoy
- B: McAllister
- C: McTavish
- D: McFly

7) £4000
Which of these is a famous golfing trophy?
- A: Wightman Cup
- B: Fed Cup
- C: Ryder Cup
- D: Calcutta Cup

8) £8,000
Complete the title of the US sitcom, '..., Indiana'?
- A: Spooky
- B: Weird
- C: Eerie
- D: Oddball

9) £16,000
Which Muppet played Bob Cratchit to Michael Caine's Scrooge in a 1992 film?
- A: Kermit
- B: Miss Piggy
- C: Animal
- D: Fozzie Bear

10) £32,000
What was the first name of Kojak, the police detective played by Telly Savalas?
- A: Dino
- B: Josh
- C: Theo
- D: Loll

You have won at least £32,000!

11) £64,000
Which of these tools shares its name with an old proverb or saying?
- A: Mallet
- B: Chisel
- C: Spanner
- D: Saw

12) £125,000
Who shot Lorna Doone in the classic novel by R D Blackmore?
- A: Hacker
- B: Carver
- C: Sniper
- D: Slicer

13) £250,000
In English pantomime, who was Harlequin's sweetheart?
- A: Celandine
- B: Clementine
- C: Columbine
- D: Cymbeline

14) £500,000
What name is given to the target in long distance archery?
- A: Jolt
- B: Brunt
- C: Clout
- D: Swipe

15) £1,000,000
In which city is the Royal Armouries Museum?
- A: Leeds
- B: London
- C: Liverpool
- D: Leicester

GAME 45 ANSWERS PAGE 64

50:50 from page 52
Ask The Audience from page 56
Phone-A-Friend

CONGRATULATIONS YOU ARE A MILLIONAIRE!

GAME 46

1) £100

The melody used to introduce and identify a radio or television programme is known as its ...?

- A: Signature tune
- B: Autograph tune
- C: Alias tune
- D: Moniker tune

2) £200

Where are the headquarters of the MCC?

- A: Lord's
- B: Lady's
- C: Sir's
- D: Madam's

3) £300

By what name is the Boeing 747 also known?

- A: Superfortress
- B: Dumbo
- C: Jumbo
- D: Tristar

4) £500

Which of these is a model of a small two-seater car?

- A: Neat Car
- B: Cute Car
- C: Chic Car
- D: Smart Car

5) £1,000

Which saint shares his name with a London mainline railway terminus?

- A: St Eustace
- B: St Pancras
- C: St Giles
- D: St Alban

You have won at least £1,000!

6) £2,000

Which creatures feature in the 2004 film 'Open Water'?

- A: Sea snakes
- B: Crocodiles
- C: Octopuses
- D: Sharks

7) £4,000

Which 'Cup' is the highlight of the Australian horseracing season?

- A: Sydney
- B: Melbourne
- C: Perth
- D: Brisbane

8) £8,000

With whom did Barbara Dickson duet on a 1985 UK No 1 single?

- A: Elaine Paige
- B: Lulu
- C: Cher
- D: Sandie Shaw

9) £16,000

A roaring lion is the symbol of which Hollywood film studio?

- A: MGM
- B: Warner Bros
- C: Paramount
- D: Universal

10) £32,000

The Knesset is the parliament of which country?

- A: Israel
- B: Turkey
- C: Greece
- D: Austria

You have won at least £32,000!

11) £64,000

The port of Famagusta is a resort on which holiday island?

- A: Cyprus
- B: Majorca
- C: Crete
- D: Minorca

12) £125,000

Together with white and red, what other colour makes up the national flag of Luxembourg?

- A: Green
- B: Blue
- C: Orange
- D: Yellow

13) £250,000

What is a croque-monsieur topped with a fried egg called?

- A: Croque supreme
- B: Croque cocotte
- C: Croque madame
- D: Croque delice

14) £500,000

In heraldic terms, which word signifies an animal in a walking position?

- A: Couchant
- B: Rampant
- C: Dormant
- D: Passant

15) £1,000,000

In Holst's 'Planets' suite, which is 'The Magician'?

- A: Jupiter
- B: Neptune
- C: Uranus
- D: Mars

GAME 46 ANSWERS PAGE 64

50:50 from page 52

Ask The Audience from page 56

Phone-A-Friend

CONGRATULATIONS YOU ARE A MILLIONAIRE!

47

GAME 47

1) £100
Which is an upper seating area in a theatre?

- A: Square
- B: Circle
- C: Rectangle
- D: Oval

2) £200
What type of 'ear' is a boxing injury?

- A: Tomato
- B: Mushroom
- C: Cauliflower
- D: Potato

3) £300
Which of these is a standard name for a colour?

- A: Jam jar blue
- B: Flagon brown
- C: Carafe red
- D: Bottle green

4) £500
To which member of the family does the word 'fraternal' refer?

- A: Father
- B: Mother
- C: Sister
- D: Brother

5) £1,000
Complete the aid to memorising the colours of the rainbow, 'Richard Of York Gained Battle ...'?

- A: In Vain
- B: In Vanity
- C: In Vantage
- D: In Vienna

You have won at least £1,000!

6) £2,000
Where was the Olympic torch first lit in March 2004?

- A: Olympia
- B: Athens
- C: Mount Olympus
- D: Marathon

7) £4,000
What does the 'O' stand for in the name of the pop duo commonly known as OMD?

- A: Orbital
- B: Ornamental
- C: Original
- D: Orchestral

8) £8,000
If you travel over the Menai Bridge from the mainland, on which island do you land?

- A: Isle of Wight
- B: Lundy
- C: Lindisfarne
- D: Anglesey

9) £16,000
Which English city was known by the Romans as Aquae Sulis?

- A: St Albans
- B: Salisbury
- C: Bristol
- D: Bath

10) £32,000
How is the British musician Mike Skinner better known?

- A: The Lanes
- B: The Alleys
- C: The Streets
- D: The Avenues

You have won at least £32,000!

11) £64,000
What is the medical term for chickenpox?

- A: Varicella
- B: Pertussis
- C: Rubella
- D: Parotitis

12) £125,000
Where in the human body is the trapezium bone?

- A: Ear
- B: Back
- C: Shoulder
- D: Wrist

13) £250,000
To which class of animals do turtles and crocodiles belong?

- A: Mammalia
- B: Reptilia
- C: Amphibia
- D: Marsupialia

14) £500,000
Who designed the food processor in 1947?

- A: Ken Wood
- B: Steve Moulinex
- C: Larry Rowenta
- D: Reg Braun

15) £1,000,000
What item of clothing is a burnous?

- A: Cloak
- B: Trousers
- C: Scarf
- D: Shirt

GAME 47 ANSWERS PAGE 64

50:50 from page 52
Ask The Audience from page 56
Phone-A-Friend

CONGRATULATIONS YOU ARE A MILLIONAIRE!

GAME 48

1) £100
Apples are the chief ingredients of which drink?
- A: Tea
- B: Port
- C: Gin
- D: Cider

2) £200
Which of these is a boxing weight?
- A: Pinweight
- B: Featherweight
- C: Longweight
- D: Overweight

3) £300
Which shape is associated with a relationship described as 'eternal'?
- A: Rectangle
- B: Cylinder
- C: Triangle
- D: Pyramid

4) £500
What is the traditional shape of a US sheriff's badge?
- A: Star
- B: Shield
- C: Crescent
- D: Gun

5) £1,000
Which of these foods is often sold 'on the vine'?
- A: Grapefruit
- B: Tomato
- C: Broccoli
- D: Potato

You have won at least £1,000!

6) £2,000
Which band released the song 'Thunderbirds are Go' in July 2004?
- A: Busted
- B: McFly
- C: Girls Aloud
- D: Basement Jaxx

7) £4,000
Which people take their name from the Latin phrase meaning 'from the beginning'?
- A: Inuit
- B: Aboriginals
- C: Aztec
- D: Mongol

8) £8,000
In the Bible, which archangel foretold the birth of Jesus?
- A: Michael
- B: Abraham
- C: Raphael
- D: Gabriel

9) £16,000
The red dragon on the Welsh national flag is standing on how many feet?
- A: None
- B: Two
- C: Three
- D: Four

10) £32,000
What term applies to a word or phrase which reads the same backwards or forwards?
- A: Mnemonic
- B: Acrostic
- C: Palindrome
- D: Anagram

You have won at least £32,000!

11) £64,000
Which inventor was known as the 'Wizard of Menlo Park'?
- A: Frank Whittle
- B: Thomas Edison
- C: Robert Boyle
- D: Orville Wright

12) £125,000
Of which sport is the Eton Wall Game a version?
- A: Cricket
- B: Squash
- C: Football
- D: Fives

13) £250,000
Which Spanish city was the birthplace of Pablo Picasso?
- A: Barcelona
- B: Cordoba
- C: Malaga
- D: Madrid

14) £500,000
In 'Gulliver's Travels', what is Swift's name for a 'brute with human form'?
- A: Hellbag
- B: Larrikin
- C: Yahoo
- D: Yegg

15) £1,000,000
What is the name of the cat belonging to Robert De Niro's character in 'Meet the Parents'?
- A: Lucky
- B: Mumbo
- C: Jinxie
- D: Hocus

GAME 48 ANSWERS PAGE 64

50:50 from page 52
Ask The Audience from page 56
Phone-A-Friend

CONGRATULATIONS YOU ARE A MILLIONAIRE!

49

GAME 49

1) £100
Which of these is a type of bear?
- A: Grumpy bear
- B: Moody bear
- C: Grizzly bear
- D: Sulky bear

2) £200
Which of these TV soaps is chiefly set in a hospital?
- A: Family Affairs
- B: Hollyoaks
- C: Casualty
- D: Neighbours

3) £300
Which is the shortest of these months?
- A: May
- B: June
- C: July
- D: August

4) £500
What is the financial term for assets which can easily be converted to cash?
- A: Molten
- B: Runny
- C: Liquid
- D: Aqueous

5) £1000
Which of these is a type of loaf?
- A: Cut can
- B: Rip jug
- C: Crack pot
- D: Split tin

You have won at least £1000!

6) £2000
Which sport-based film starring Paul Bettany was released in the UK during 2004?
- A: Monte Carlo
- B: Wimbledon
- C: St Andrews
- D: Cowes

7) £4000
Which of these is the third planet from our Sun?
- A: Mercury
- B: Earth
- C: Venus
- D: Mars

8) £8,000
In which sport might you suffer a 'wipe out'?
- A: Surfing
- B: Gymnastics
- C: Squash
- D: Bowling

9) £16,000
Which of these inventions is attributed to James Watt?
- A: Steam engine
- B: Spinning jenny
- C: Water frame
- D: Safety lamp

10) £32,000
What is the name for the compass housing on board a ship?
- A: Halyard
- B: Drogue
- C: Binnacle
- D: Cringle

You have won at least £32,000!

11) £64,000
Whose backing group were the Dinosaurs?
- A: Bruno Saurus
- B: T. Rex
- C: Try Ceratops
- D: Terry Dactyl

12) £125,000
Who wrote the blockbuster novel 'The Eagle Has Landed'?
- A: Robert Ludlum
- B: John Grisham
- C: Jack Higgins
- D: Eric Ambler

13) £250,000
What is the lowest number not designated to a British motorway?
- A: 7
- B: 8
- C: 9
- D: 10

14) £500,000
In 'Don Quixote', what is the name of Sancho Panza's donkey?
- A: Dapple
- B: Beauty
- C: Blackie
- D: Silver

15) £1,000,000
What name did Ulrika Jonsson give her baby girl born in May 2004?
- A: Molly
- B: Minty
- C: Martha
- D: Mia

GAME 49
ANSWERS
PAGE 64

50:50
from page 52

Ask The Audience
from page 56

Phone-A-Friend

CONGRATULATIONS YOU ARE A MILLIONAIRE!

GAME 50

1) £100
Which finger is positioned next to the thumb?
- A: Epilogue
- B: Index
- C: Foreword
- D: Appendix

2) £200
What name is given to the narrow waterways found in Norway?
- A: Fjords
- B: Vauxhalls
- C: Nissans
- D: Hondas

3) £300
In the armed forces, which instrument is most likely to sound the last post?
- A: Sousaphone
- B: Bugle
- C: Tuba
- D: Snare drum

4) £500
Which song won Dido an Ivor Novello Award in 2004?
- A: White Flag
- B: Red Banner
- C: Blue Badge
- D: Green Standard

5) £1,000
'Motorcade' is a combination of 'motor' and which other word?
- A: Palisade
- B: Carronade
- C: Cavalcade
- D: Esplanade

You have won at least £1,000!

6) £2,000
Which footballer was chosen as the 2004 face of Vodafone and Adidas?
- A: David Beckham
- B: Ashley Cole
- C: Jamie Redknapp
- D: Michael Owen

7) £4,000
By what stage name is the comedian Jim Moir better known?
- A: Vic Reeves
- B: Peter Kay
- C: Frank Skinner
- D: Johnny Vegas

8) £8,000
Which Andrew was the BBC journalist at the centre of the Iraq weapons dossier furore?
- A: Milligan
- B: Finnegan
- C: Gilligan
- D: Mulligan

9) £16,000
Which means of communication was invented by Lazarus Ludwig Zamenhof?
- A: Morse code
- B: Semaphore
- C: Esperanto
- D: Interlingua

10) £32,000
What forename links a British prime minister, John Lennon and Gary Lineker?
- A: William
- B: Walter
- C: Wesley
- D: Winston

You have won at least £32,000!

11) £64,000
The 'Guns N' Roses' 1987 album is entitled 'Appetite for ...'?
- A: Illusion
- B: Retribution
- C: Annihilation
- D: Destruction

12) £125,000
What type of garment is a tarboosh?
- A: Shoe
- B: Hat
- C: Shirt
- D: Jacket

13) £250,000
Which play by David Hare, first performed in 2004, is about the origins of the Iraq War?
- A: The Judas Kiss
- B: Stuff Happens
- C: Pravda
- D: Via Dolorosa

14) £500,000
Which author won the 2004 Whitbread Prize?
- A: D B C Pierre
- B: Don Paterson
- C: Mark Haddon
- D: David Almond

15) £1,000,000
Which music legend was made a Doctor of Music at St Andrews University in 2004?
- A: Mark Knopfler
- B: Eric Clapton
- C: Bob Dylan
- D: Paul McCartney

GAME 50 ANSWERS PAGE 64

50:50 from page 52
Ask The Audience from page 56
Phone-A-Friend

CONGRATULATIONS YOU ARE A MILLIONAIRE!

£100

Game 1. Options remaining are B and C
Game 2. Options remaining are B and C
Game 3. Options remaining are B and D
Game 4. Options remaining are A and C
Game 5. Options remaining are B and C
Game 6. Options remaining are A and D
Game 7. Options remaining are A and C
Game 8. Options remaining are A and C
Game 9. Options remaining are B and C
Game 10. Options remaining are B and C
Game 11. Options remaining are B and C
Game 12. Options remaining are B and C
Game 13. Options remaining are B and D
Game 14. Options remaining are A and D
Game 15. Options remaining are A and D
Game 16. Options remaining are B and C
Game 17. Options remaining are A and B
Game 18. Options remaining are B and C
Game 19. Options remaining are A and B
Game 20. Options remaining are C and D
Game 21. Options remaining are B and D
Game 22. Options remaining are B and D
Game 23. Options remaining are A and D
Game 24. Options remaining are B and D
Game 25. Options remaining are B and D
Game 26. Options remaining are B and D
Game 27. Options remaining are B and D
Game 28. Options remaining are A and C
Game 29. Options remaining are A and B
Game 30. Options remaining are A and C
Game 31. Options remaining are B and C
Game 32. Options remaining are B and C
Game 33. Options remaining are A and C
Game 34. Options remaining are A and B
Game 35. Options remaining are B and D
Game 36. Options remaining are C and D
Game 37. Options remaining are B and D
Game 38. Options remaining are B and D
Game 39. Options remaining are A and C
Game 40. Options remaining are B and C
Game 41. Options remaining are C and D
Game 42. Options remaining are B and D
Game 43. Options remaining are B and C
Game 44. Options remaining are B and D
Game 45. Options remaining are B and D
Game 46. Options remaining are A and B
Game 47. Options remaining are B and D
Game 48. Options remaining are A and D
Game 49. Options remaining are C and D
Game 50. Options remaining are B and D

£200

Game 1. Options remaining are B and D
Game 2. Options remaining are B and C
Game 3. Options remaining are A and C
Game 4. Options remaining are B and D
Game 5. Options remaining are A and B
Game 6. Options remaining are A and C
Game 7. Options remaining are B and D
Game 8. Options remaining are A and B
Game 9. Options remaining are B and D
Game 10. Options remaining are A and C
Game 11. Options remaining are B and D
Game 12. Options remaining are C and D

Game 13. Options remaining are A and C
Game 14. Options remaining are C and D
Game 15. Options remaining are C and D
Game 16. Options remaining are A and D
Game 17. Options remaining are B and C
Game 18. Options remaining are C and D
Game 19. Options remaining are B and D
Game 20. Options remaining are B and C
Game 21. Options remaining are A and B
Game 22. Options remaining are C and D
Game 23. Options remaining are A and D
Game 24. Options remaining are A and C
Game 25. Options remaining are B and D
Game 26. Options remaining are A and C
Game 27. Options remaining are B and D
Game 28. Options remaining are A and C
Game 29. Options remaining are A and C
Game 30. Options remaining are A and C
Game 31. Options remaining are A and B
Game 32. Options remaining are A and C
Game 33. Options remaining are B and C
Game 34. Options remaining are A and B
Game 35. Options remaining are A and D
Game 36. Options remaining are A and C
Game 37. Options remaining are B and C
Game 38. Options remaining are B and C
Game 39. Options remaining are B and C
Game 40. Options remaining are B and D
Game 41. Options remaining are B and D
Game 42. Options remaining are B and C
Game 43. Options remaining are C and D
Game 44. Options remaining are B and D
Game 45. Options remaining are A and B
Game 46. Options remaining are A and B
Game 47. Options remaining are A and C
Game 48. Options remaining are A and B
Game 49. Options remaining are B and C
Game 50. Options remaining are A and C

£300

Game 1. Options remaining are A and B
Game 2. Options remaining are A and B
Game 3. Options remaining are C and D
Game 4. Options remaining are A and D
Game 5. Options remaining are A and C
Game 6. Options remaining are A and B
Game 7. Options remaining are A and C
Game 8. Options remaining are C and D
Game 9. Options remaining are A and D
Game 10. Options remaining are B and D
Game 11. Options remaining are A and D
Game 12. Options remaining are B and C
Game 13. Options remaining are C and D
Game 14. Options remaining are A and C
Game 15. Options remaining are B and D
Game 16. Options remaining are A and D
Game 17. Options remaining are A and D
Game 18. Options remaining are A and B
Game 19. Options remaining are C and D
Game 20. Options remaining are C and D
Game 21. Options remaining are A and D
Game 22. Options remaining are A and D
Game 23. Options remaining are A and C
Game 24. Options remaining are A and C
Game 25. Options remaining are A and D

£400

Game 26. Options remaining are B and C
Game 27. Options remaining are A and B
Game 28. Options remaining are A and C
Game 29. Options remaining are A and D
Game 30. Options remaining are B and D
Game 31. Options remaining are B and D
Game 32. Options remaining are A and D
Game 33. Options remaining are A and C
Game 34. Options remaining are A and C
Game 35. Options remaining are A and C
Game 36. Options remaining are B and D
Game 37. Options remaining are C and D
Game 38. Options remaining are C and D
Game 39. Options remaining are B and C
Game 40. Options remaining are A and D
Game 41. Options remaining are B and C
Game 42. Options remaining are B and D
Game 43. Options remaining are C and D
Game 44. Options remaining are A and C
Game 45. Options remaining are B and D
Game 46. Options remaining are C and D
Game 47. Options remaining are B and D
Game 48. Options remaining are C and D
Game 49. Options remaining are B and C
Game 50. Options remaining are B and D

£500

Game 1. Options remaining are A and D
Game 2. Options remaining are B and C
Game 3. Options remaining are C and D
Game 4. Options remaining are A and D
Game 5. Options remaining are A and C
Game 6. Options remaining are B and C
Game 7. Options remaining are A and C
Game 8. Options remaining are A and C
Game 9. Options remaining are B and D
Game 10. Options remaining are A and D
Game 11. Options remaining are B and D
Game 12. Options remaining are A and D
Game 13. Options remaining are A and C
Game 14. Options remaining are A and B
Game 15. Options remaining are B and D
Game 16. Options remaining are B and D
Game 17. Options remaining are B and C
Game 18. Options remaining are A and C
Game 19. Options remaining are B and C
Game 20. Options remaining are A and C
Game 21. Options remaining are B and C
Game 22. Options remaining are A and D
Game 23. Options remaining are B and C
Game 24. Options remaining are A and D
Game 25. Options remaining are B and D
Game 26. Options remaining are B and C
Game 27. Options remaining are A and C
Game 28. Options remaining are A and C
Game 29. Options remaining are C and D
Game 30. Options remaining are A and D
Game 31. Options remaining are A and B
Game 32. Options remaining are A and C
Game 33. Options remaining are B and C
Game 34. Options remaining are A and D
Game 35. Options remaining are B and D
Game 36. Options remaining are C and D
Game 37. Options remaining are A and D
Game 38. Options remaining are C and D

Game 39. Options remaining are A and B
Game 40. Options remaining are C and D
Game 41. Options remaining are B and C
Game 42. Options remaining are A and C
Game 43. Options remaining are A and C
Game 44. Options remaining are A and D
Game 45. Options remaining are C and D
Game 46. Options remaining are C and D
Game 47. Options remaining are A and D
Game 48. Options remaining are A and C
Game 49. Options remaining are A and C
Game 50. Options remaining are A and B

£1,000

Game 1. Options remaining are B and C
Game 2. Options remaining are B and C
Game 3. Options remaining are A and C
Game 4. Options remaining are A and C
Game 5. Options remaining are A and D
Game 6. Options remaining are C and D
Game 7. Options remaining are A and B
Game 8. Options remaining are A and C
Game 9. Options remaining are B and D
Game 10. Options remaining are A and C
Game 11. Options remaining are A and C
Game 12. Options remaining are A and C
Game 13. Options remaining are A and C
Game 14. Options remaining are B and D
Game 15. Options remaining are A and B
Game 16. Options remaining are A and B
Game 17. Options remaining are B and D
Game 18. Options remaining are A and D
Game 19. Options remaining are C and D
Game 20. Options remaining are C and D
Game 21. Options remaining are A and B
Game 22. Options remaining are A and D
Game 23. Options remaining are A and B
Game 24. Options remaining are A and D
Game 25. Options remaining are A and C
Game 26. Options remaining are A and D
Game 27. Options remaining are B and C
Game 28. Options remaining are B and D
Game 29. Options remaining are A and C
Game 30. Options remaining are B and D
Game 31. Options remaining are A and C
Game 32. Options remaining are B and D
Game 33. Options remaining are A and B
Game 34. Options remaining are C and D
Game 35. Options remaining are C and D
Game 36. Options remaining are A and D
Game 37. Options remaining are C and D
Game 38. Options remaining are A and C
Game 39. Options remaining are A and B
Game 40. Options remaining are A and D
Game 41. Options remaining are C and D
Game 42. Options remaining are B and D
Game 43. Options remaining are A and D
Game 44. Options remaining are A and C
Game 45. Options remaining are A and C
Game 46. Options remaining are A and B
Game 47. Options remaining are A and D
Game 48. Options remaining are A and B
Game 49. Options remaining are A and D
Game 50. Options remaining are A and C

£2,000

Game 1. Options remaining are B and C
Game 2. Options remaining are A and B
Game 3. Options remaining are B and C
Game 4. Options remaining are A and C
Game 5. Options remaining are C and D
Game 6. Options remaining are A and C
Game 7. Options remaining are A and D
Game 8. Options remaining are C and D
Game 9. Options remaining are B and C
Game 10. Options remaining are B and D
Game 11. Options remaining are C and D
Game 12. Options remaining are B and C
Game 13. Options remaining are B and C
Game 14. Options remaining are A and C
Game 15. Options remaining are A and B
Game 16. Options remaining are B and C
Game 17. Options remaining are B and C
Game 18. Options remaining are B and D
Game 19. Options remaining are A and C
Game 20. Options remaining are A and C
Game 21. Options remaining are A and C
Game 22. Options remaining are C and D
Game 23. Options remaining are B and C
Game 24. Options remaining are A and D
Game 25. Options remaining are C and D
Game 26. Options remaining are B and D
Game 27. Options remaining are A and D
Game 28. Options remaining are A and B
Game 29. Options remaining are B and D
Game 30. Options remaining are C and D
Game 31. Options remaining are A and B
Game 32. Options remaining are A and D
Game 33. Options remaining are A and B
Game 34. Options remaining are B and C
Game 35. Options remaining are A and D
Game 36. Options remaining are B and D
Game 37. Options remaining are A and D
Game 38. Options remaining are B and D
Game 39. Options remaining are B and C
Game 40. Options remaining are A and D
Game 41. Options remaining are C and D
Game 42. Options remaining are C and D
Game 43. Options remaining are B and C
Game 44. Options remaining are B and C
Game 45. Options remaining are A and D
Game 46. Options remaining are B and D
Game 47. Options remaining are A and C
Game 48. Options remaining are A and D
Game 49. Options remaining are B and D
Game 50. Options remaining are A and C

£4,000

Game 1. Options remaining are B and C
Game 2. Options remaining are B and D
Game 3. Options remaining are A and D
Game 4. Options remaining are B and C
Game 5. Options remaining are A and D
Game 6. Options remaining are C and D
Game 7. Options remaining are B and C
Game 8. Options remaining are A and B
Game 9. Options remaining are B and D
Game 10. Options remaining are C and D
Game 11. Options remaining are A and C
Game 12. Options remaining are A and D

Game 13. Options remaining are A and D
Game 14. Options remaining are A and D
Game 15. Options remaining are B and D
Game 16. Options remaining are A and D
Game 17. Options remaining are B and C
Game 18. Options remaining are C and D
Game 19. Options remaining are A and C
Game 20. Options remaining are A and C
Game 21. Options remaining are A and B
Game 22. Options remaining are C and D
Game 23. Options remaining are A and C
Game 24. Options remaining are B and C
Game 25. Options remaining are B and C
Game 26. Options remaining are B and D
Game 27. Options remaining are A and B
Game 28. Options remaining are B and D
Game 29. Options remaining are A and C
Game 30. Options remaining are C and D
Game 31. Options remaining are A and B
Game 32. Options remaining are C and D
Game 33. Options remaining are B and C
Game 34. Options remaining are A and B
Game 35. Options remaining are B and C
Game 36. Options remaining are A and B
Game 37. Options remaining are A and D
Game 38. Options remaining are A and B
Game 39. Options remaining are A and B
Game 40. Options remaining are B and D
Game 41. Options remaining are A and D
Game 42. Options remaining are B and C
Game 43. Options remaining are A and C
Game 44. Options remaining are A and D
Game 45. Options remaining are C and D
Game 46. Options remaining are B and D
Game 47. Options remaining are B and D
Game 48. Options remaining are A and B
Game 49. Options remaining are A and B
Game 50. Options remaining are A and D

£8,000

Game 1. Options remaining are A and B
Game 2. Options remaining are A and C
Game 3. Options remaining are A and B
Game 4. Options remaining are A and B
Game 5. Options remaining are A and D
Game 6. Options remaining are A and B
Game 7. Options remaining are B and D
Game 8. Options remaining are A and D
Game 9. Options remaining are B and D
Game 10. Options remaining are A and C
Game 11. Options remaining are C and D
Game 12. Options remaining are B and D
Game 13. Options remaining are C and D
Game 14. Options remaining are A and D
Game 15. Options remaining are B and D
Game 16. Options remaining are A and D
Game 17. Options remaining are C and D
Game 18. Options remaining are B and D
Game 19. Options remaining are A and C
Game 20. Options remaining are C and D
Game 21. Options remaining are A and B
Game 22. Options remaining are C and D
Game 23. Options remaining are A and C
Game 24. Options remaining are B and D
Game 25. Options remaining are A and C

Game 26. Options remaining are B and C
Game 27. Options remaining are A and B
Game 28. Options remaining are A and C
Game 29. Options remaining are A and C
Game 30. Options remaining are A and B
Game 31. Options remaining are A and C
Game 32. Options remaining are A and B
Game 33. Options remaining are B and D
Game 34. Options remaining are B and C
Game 35. Options remaining are A and D
Game 36. Options remaining are C and D
Game 37. Options remaining are A and C
Game 38. Options remaining are A and B
Game 39. Options remaining are B and C
Game 40. Options remaining are B and D
Game 41. Options remaining are B and D
Game 42. Options remaining are B and C
Game 43. Options remaining are C and D
Game 44. Options remaining are A and C
Game 45. Options remaining are C and D
Game 46. Options remaining are A and D
Game 47. Options remaining are C and D
Game 48. Options remaining are A and D
Game 49. Options remaining are A and C
Game 50. Options remaining are A and C

£16,000
Game 1. Options remaining are B and D
Game 2. Options remaining are A and D
Game 3. Options remaining are A and C
Game 4. Options remaining are B and D
Game 5. Options remaining are A and C
Game 6. Options remaining are A and B
Game 7. Options remaining are A and B
Game 8. Options remaining are B and D
Game 9. Options remaining are B and C
Game 10. Options remaining are B and D
Game 11. Options remaining are C and D
Game 12. Options remaining are A and B
Game 13. Options remaining are A and D
Game 14. Options remaining are B and C
Game 15. Options remaining are A and C
Game 16. Options remaining are B and C
Game 17. Options remaining are A and C
Game 18. Options remaining are A and D
Game 19. Options remaining are A and D
Game 20. Options remaining are B and C
Game 21. Options remaining are A and C
Game 22. Options remaining are A and C
Game 23. Options remaining are B and D
Game 24. Options remaining are C and D
Game 25. Options remaining are C and D
Game 26. Options remaining are A and B
Game 27. Options remaining are B and D
Game 28. Options remaining are A and C
Game 29. Options remaining are B and D
Game 30. Options remaining are B and D
Game 31. Options remaining are B and C
Game 32. Options remaining are C and D
Game 33. Options remaining are C and D
Game 34. Options remaining are B and C
Game 35. Options remaining are A and B
Game 36. Options remaining are B and D
Game 37. Options remaining are A and D
Game 38. Options remaining are A and B

Game 39. Options remaining are B and D
Game 40. Options remaining are A and D
Game 41. Options remaining are B and C
Game 42. Options remaining are A and D
Game 43. Options remaining are A and C
Game 44. Options remaining are A and C
Game 45. Options remaining are A and C
Game 46. Options remaining are A and C
Game 47. Options remaining are B and D
Game 48. Options remaining are B and C
Game 49. Options remaining are A and C
Game 50. Options remaining are C and D

£32,000
Game 1. Options remaining are B and C
Game 2. Options remaining are B and D
Game 3. Options remaining are B and C
Game 4. Options remaining are A and C
Game 5. Options remaining are A and B
Game 6. Options remaining are C and D
Game 7. Options remaining are B and C
Game 8. Options remaining are C and D
Game 9. Options remaining are B and C
Game 10. Options remaining are A and C
Game 11. Options remaining are A and C
Game 12. Options remaining are A and B
Game 13. Options remaining are B and D
Game 14. Options remaining are B and C
Game 15. Options remaining are C and D
Game 16. Options remaining are C and D
Game 17. Options remaining are C and D
Game 18. Options remaining are C and D
Game 19. Options remaining are A and D
Game 20. Options remaining are B and D
Game 21. Options remaining are A and B
Game 22. Options remaining are A and C
Game 23. Options remaining are A and C
Game 24. Options remaining are A and B
Game 25. Options remaining are A and C
Game 26. Options remaining are C and D
Game 27. Options remaining are C and D
Game 28. Options remaining are A and C
Game 29. Options remaining are C and D
Game 30. Options remaining are C and D
Game 31. Options remaining are A and B
Game 32. Options remaining are A and C
Game 33. Options remaining are C and D
Game 34. Options remaining are B and D
Game 35. Options remaining are A and B
Game 36. Options remaining are A and D
Game 37. Options remaining are A and B
Game 38. Options remaining are A and B
Game 39. Options remaining are A and C
Game 40. Options remaining are B and D
Game 41. Options remaining are A and C
Game 42. Options remaining are A and C
Game 43. Options remaining are B and C
Game 44. Options remaining are C and D
Game 45. Options remaining are A and C
Game 46. Options remaining are A and C
Game 47. Options remaining are A and C
Game 48. Options remaining are B and C
Game 49. Options remaining are C and D
Game 50. Options remaining are A and D

£64,000
Game 1. Options remaining are B and C
Game 2. Options remaining are B and D
Game 3. Options remaining are B and D
Game 4. Options remaining are C and D
Game 5. Options remaining are A and C
Game 6. Options remaining are A and B
Game 7. Options remaining are B and C
Game 8. Options remaining are A and D
Game 9. Options remaining are B and D
Game 10. Options remaining are B and D
Game 11. Options remaining are B and C
Game 12. Options remaining are A and B
Game 13. Options remaining are C and D
Game 14. Options remaining are B and C
Game 15. Options remaining are B and D
Game 16. Options remaining are B and D
Game 17. Options remaining are A and B
Game 18. Options remaining are B and D
Game 19. Options remaining are B and C
Game 20. Options remaining are A and D
Game 21. Options remaining are B and C
Game 22. Options remaining are B and D
Game 23. Options remaining are A and D
Game 24. Options remaining are A and C
Game 25. Options remaining are A and C
Game 26. Options remaining are A and D
Game 27. Options remaining are B and D
Game 28. Options remaining are A and B
Game 29. Options remaining are A and D
Game 30. Options remaining are A and B
Game 31. Options remaining are B and C
Game 32. Options remaining are B and D
Game 33. Options remaining are A and B
Game 34. Options remaining are A and D
Game 35. Options remaining are A and B
Game 36. Options remaining are B and D
Game 37. Options remaining are C and D
Game 38. Options remaining are B and D
Game 39. Options remaining are C and D
Game 40. Options remaining are C and D
Game 41. Options remaining are C and D
Game 42. Options remaining are A and B
Game 43. Options remaining are C and D
Game 44. Options remaining are B and D
Game 45. Options remaining are C and D
Game 46. Options remaining are A and B
Game 47. Options remaining are A and B
Game 48. Options remaining are A and B
Game 49. Options remaining are A and D
Game 50. Options remaining are A and D

£125,000
Game 1. Options remaining are B and C
Game 2. Options remaining are B and D
Game 3. Options remaining are A and D
Game 4. Options remaining are A and B
Game 5. Options remaining are B and C
Game 6. Options remaining are A and C
Game 7. Options remaining are B and C
Game 8. Options remaining are A and B
Game 9. Options remaining are A and D
Game 10. Options remaining are C and D
Game 11. Options remaining are A and B
Game 12. Options remaining are B and D

Game 13. Options remaining are B and C
Game 14. Options remaining are A and D
Game 15. Options remaining are A and D
Game 16. Options remaining are A and C
Game 17. Options remaining are B and D
Game 18. Options remaining are A and C
Game 19. Options remaining are B and D
Game 20. Options remaining are A and D
Game 21. Options remaining are A and C
Game 22. Options remaining are B and C
Game 23. Options remaining are B and C
Game 24. Options remaining are B and D
Game 25. Options remaining are A and C
Game 26. Options remaining are A and C
Game 27. Options remaining are C and D
Game 28. Options remaining are A and C
Game 29. Options remaining are C and D
Game 30. Options remaining are B and D
Game 31. Options remaining are A and C
Game 32. Options remaining are B and C
Game 33. Options remaining are C and D
Game 34. Options remaining are A and B
Game 35. Options remaining are C and D
Game 36. Options remaining are B and D
Game 37. Options remaining are A and C
Game 38. Options remaining are A and B
Game 39. Options remaining are B and D
Game 40. Options remaining are B and D
Game 41. Options remaining are C and D
Game 42. Options remaining are B and C
Game 43. Options remaining are A and D
Game 44. Options remaining are B and D
Game 45. Options remaining are A and B
Game 46. Options remaining are B and C
Game 47. Options remaining are C and D
Game 48. Options remaining are C and D
Game 49. Options remaining are B and C
Game 50. Options remaining are B and C

£250,000

Game 1. Options remaining are B and C
Game 2. Options remaining are A and C
Game 3. Options remaining are B and D
Game 4. Options remaining are A and C
Game 5. Options remaining are B and C
Game 6. Options remaining are B and D
Game 7. Options remaining are B and D
Game 8. Options remaining are B and C
Game 9. Options remaining are A and C
Game 10. Options remaining are C and D
Game 11. Options remaining are C and D
Game 12. Options remaining are B and D
Game 13. Options remaining are B and C
Game 14. Options remaining are C and D
Game 15. Options remaining are B and C
Game 16. Options remaining are B and D
Game 17. Options remaining are B and C
Game 18. Options remaining are B and C
Game 19. Options remaining are C and D
Game 20. Options remaining are A and C
Game 21. Options remaining are A and B
Game 22. Options remaining are A and D
Game 23. Options remaining are A and C
Game 24. Options remaining are A and B
Game 25. Options remaining are A and B

Game 26. Options remaining are C and D
Game 27. Options remaining are A and C
Game 28. Options remaining are B and C
Game 29. Options remaining are A and B
Game 30. Options remaining are A and D
Game 31. Options remaining are A and D
Game 32. Options remaining are A and C
Game 33. Options remaining are B and C
Game 34. Options remaining are B and D
Game 35. Options remaining are A and D
Game 36. Options remaining are A and C
Game 37. Options remaining are B and C
Game 38. Options remaining are A and B
Game 39. Options remaining are B and C
Game 40. Options remaining are B and C
Game 41. Options remaining are B and C
Game 42. Options remaining are C and D
Game 43. Options remaining are B and C
Game 44. Options remaining are B and C
Game 45. Options remaining are C and D
Game 46. Options remaining are B and C
Game 47. Options remaining are B and C
Game 48. Options remaining are B and C
Game 49. Options remaining are A and D
Game 50. Options remaining are B and D

£500,000

Game 1. Options remaining are A and D
Game 2. Options remaining are A and C
Game 3. Options remaining are C and D
Game 4. Options remaining are B and D
Game 5. Options remaining are B and C
Game 6. Options remaining are A and D
Game 7. Options remaining are B and D
Game 8. Options remaining are A and C
Game 9. Options remaining are B and D
Game 10. Options remaining are A and C
Game 11. Options remaining are A and D
Game 12. Options remaining are C and D
Game 13. Options remaining are B and D
Game 14. Options remaining are B and C
Game 15. Options remaining are B and D
Game 16. Options remaining are C and D
Game 17. Options remaining are A and C
Game 18. Options remaining are A and D
Game 19. Options remaining are B and C
Game 20. Options remaining are A and D
Game 21. Options remaining are A and C
Game 22. Options remaining are A and C
Game 23. Options remaining are A and D
Game 24. Options remaining are A and B
Game 25. Options remaining are B and D
Game 26. Options remaining are B and C
Game 27. Options remaining are B and C
Game 28. Options remaining are A and C
Game 29. Options remaining are B and D
Game 30. Options remaining are A and C
Game 31. Options remaining are C and D
Game 32. Options remaining are A and C
Game 33. Options remaining are A and C
Game 34. Options remaining are A and B
Game 35. Options remaining are B and D
Game 36. Options remaining are B and C
Game 37. Options remaining are A and B
Game 38. Options remaining are A and D

Game 39. Options remaining are A and C
Game 40. Options remaining are A and B
Game 41. Options remaining are A and C
Game 42. Options remaining are C and D
Game 43. Options remaining are B and D
Game 44. Options remaining are A and C
Game 45. Options remaining are B and C
Game 46. Options remaining are A and D
Game 47. Options remaining are A and D
Game 48. Options remaining are C and D
Game 49. Options remaining are A and B
Game 50. Options remaining are A and C

£100,000,000

Game 1. Options remaining are A and D
Game 2. Options remaining are C and D
Game 3. Options remaining are B and D
Game 4. Options remaining are A and C
Game 5. Options remaining are A and C
Game 6. Options remaining are A and C
Game 7. Options remaining are A and D
Game 8. Options remaining are A and C
Game 9. Options remaining are B and C
Game 10. Options remaining are B and C
Game 11. Options remaining are B and C
Game 12. Options remaining are A and B
Game 13. Options remaining are A and B
Game 14. Options remaining are B and C
Game 15. Options remaining are B and C
Game 16. Options remaining are B and D
Game 17. Options remaining are A and D
Game 18. Options remaining are C and D
Game 19. Options remaining are A and C
Game 20. Options remaining are A and C
Game 21. Options remaining are C and D
Game 22. Options remaining are A and C
Game 23. Options remaining are A and D
Game 24. Options remaining are B and C
Game 25. Options remaining are A and C
Game 26. Options remaining are C and D
Game 27. Options remaining are A and C
Game 28. Options remaining are B and D
Game 29. Options remaining are B and C
Game 30. Options remaining are B and D
Game 31. Options remaining are A and D
Game 32. Options remaining are A and D
Game 33. Options remaining are B and C
Game 34. Options remaining are A and C
Game 35. Options remaining are B and C
Game 36. Options remaining are B and D
Game 37. Options remaining are A and D
Game 38. Options remaining are B and D
Game 39. Options remaining are B and D
Game 40. Options remaining are B and C
Game 41. Options remaining are A and C
Game 42. Options remaining are B and C
Game 43. Options remaining are C and D
Game 44. Options remaining are A and C
Game 45. Options remaining are A and C
Game 46. Options remaining are B and C
Game 47. Options remaining are A and C
Game 48. Options remaining are A and C
Game 49. Options remaining are B and C
Game 50. Options remaining are B and C

£100

Game 1.   A: 1%   B: 5%   C: 94%   D: 0%
Game 2.   A: 3%   B: 90%   C: 4%   D: 3%
Game 3.   A: 2%   B: 97%   C: 1%   D: 0%
Game 4.   A: 6%   B: 3%   C: 89%   D: 2%
Game 5.   A: 0%   B: 98%   C: 1%   D: 1%
Game 6.   A: 98%   B: 1%   C: 1%   D: 0%
Game 7.   A: 85%   B: 2%   C: 3%   D: 10%
Game 8.   A: 1%   B: 0%   C: 99%   D: 0%
Game 9.   A: 1%   B: 0%   C: 96%   D: 3%
Game 10. A: 2%   B: 95%   C: 0%   D: 3%
Game 11. A: 4%   B: 2%   C: 91%   D: 3%
Game 12. A: 1%   B: 4%   C: 90%   D: 5%
Game 13. A: 1%   B: 99%   C: 0%   D: 0%
Game 14. A: 1%   B: 3%   C: 5%   D: 91%
Game 15. A: 4%   B: 0%   C: 4%   D: 92%
Game 16. A: 4%   B: 85%   C: 10%   D: 1%
Game 17. A: 96%   B: 1%   C: 1%   D: 2%
Game 18. A: 0%   B: 1%   C: 95%   D: 4%
Game 19. A: 4%   B: 95%   C: 1%   D: 0%
Game 20. A: 5%   B: 4%   C: 96%   D: 0%
Game 21. A: 0%   B: 1%   C: 5%   D: 94%
Game 22. A: 0%   B: 0%   C: 1%   D: 99%
Game 23. A: 0%   B: 1%   C: 0%   D: 99%
Game 24. A: 0%   B: 97%   C: 3%   D: 0%
Game 25. A: 1%   B: 2%   C: 2%   D: 95%
Game 26. A: 1%   B: 98%   C: 1%   D: 0%
Game 27. A: 1%   B: 0%   C: 0%   D: 99%
Game 28. A: 3%   B: 25%   C: 70%   D: 2%
Game 29. A: 30%   B: 60%   C: 6%   D: 4%
Game 30. A: 2%   B: 1%   C: 97%   D: 0%
Game 31. A: 3%   B: 90%   C: 2%   D: 5%
Game 32. A: 1%   B: 1%   C: 95%   D: 3%
Game 33. A: 99%   B: 1%   C: 0%   D: 0%
Game 34. A: 97%   B: 0%   C: 3%   D: 0%
Game 35. A: 0%   B: 1%   C: 4%   D: 95%
Game 36. A: 2%   B: 1%   C: 1%   D: 96%
Game 37. A: 8%   B: 90%   C: 0%   D: 2%
Game 38. A: 0%   B: 99%   C: 1%   D: 0%
Game 39. A: 1%   B: 10%   C: 81%   D: 8%
Game 40. A: 0%   B: 1%   C: 95%   D: 4%
Game 41. A: 5%   B: 1%   C: 4%   D: 90%
Game 42. A: 1%   B: 1%   C: 0%   D: 98%
Game 43. A: 1%   B: 0%   C: 99%   D: 0%
Game 44. A: 0%   B: 93%   C: 5%   D: 2%
Game 45. A: 0%   B: 2%   C: 1%   D: 97%
Game 46. A: 92%   B: 6%   C: 0%   D: 2%
Game 47. A: 0%   B: 95%   C: 0%   D: 5%
Game 48. A: 1%   B: 3%   C: 0%   D: 96%
Game 49. A: 0%   B: 5%   C: 90%   D: 5%
Game 50. A: 2%   B: 96%   C: 2%   D: 0%

£200

Game 1.   A: 9%   B: 1%   C: 0%   D: 90%
Game 2.   A: 4%   B: 90%   C: 2%   D: 4%
Game 3.   A: 3%   B: 1%   C: 95%   D: 1%
Game 4.   A: 0%   B: 100% C: 0%   D: 0%
Game 5.   A: 20%   B: 70%   C: 5%   D: 5%
Game 6.   A: 1%   B: 1%   C: 98%   D: 0%
Game 7.   A: 1%   B: 95%   C: 0%   D: 4%
Game 8.   A: 97%   B: 0%   C: 2%   D: 1%
Game 9.   A: 3%   B: 90%   C: 4%   D: 3%
Game 10. A: 0%   B: 1%   C: 98%   D: 1%
Game 11. A: 0%   B: 99%   C: 1%   D: 0%
Game 12. A: 3%   B: 4%   C: 2%   D: 91%
Game 13. A: 1%   B: 4%   C: 90%   D: 5%
Game 14. A: 3%   B: 5%   C: 1%   D: 91%
Game 15. A: 1%   B: 4%   C: 10%   D: 84%
Game 16. A: 96%   B: 1%   C: 1%   D: 2%
Game 17. A: 0%   B: 1%   C: 99%   D: 0%
Game 18. A: 5%   B: 0%   C: 95%   D: 0%
Game 19. A: 0%   B: 1%   C: 0%   D: 99%
Game 20. A: 0%   B: 3%   C: 97%   D: 10%
Game 21. A: 1%   B: 95%   C: 2%   D: 2%
Game 22. A: 1%   B: 0%   C: 99%   D: 0%
Game 23. A: 0%   B: 0%   C: 1%   D: 99%
Game 24. A: 0%   B: 10%   C: 87%   D: 3%
Game 25. A: 0%   B: 1%   C: 0%   D: 99%
Game 26. A: 1%   B: 1%   C: 95%   D: 3%
Game 27. A: 0%   B: 1%   C: 0%   D: 99%
Game 28. A: 3%   B: 0%   C: 97%   D: 0%
Game 29. A: 5%   B: 0%   C: 90%   D: 5%
Game 30. A: 96%   B: 4%   C: 0%   D: 0%
Game 31. A: 4%   B: 91%   C: 5%   D: 0%
Game 32. A: 90%   B: 2%   C: 8%   D: 0%
Game 33. A: 0%   B: 4%   C: 95%   D: 1%
Game 34. A: 10%   B: 81%   C: 8%   D: 1%
Game 35. A: 1%   B: 4%   C: 0%   D: 95%
Game 36. A: 0%   B: 2%   C: 93%   D: 5%
Game 37. A: 0%   B: 98%   C: 2%   D: 0%
Game 38. A: 5%   B: 1%   C: 90%   D: 4%
Game 39. A: 0%   B: 93%   C: 5%   D: 2%
Game 40. A: 0%   B: 99%   C: 1%   D: 0%
Game 41. A: 5%   B: 90%   C: 1%   D: 4%
Game 42. A: 5%   B: 0%   C: 95%   D: 0%
Game 43. A: 4%   B: 1%   C: 95%   D: 0%
Game 44. A: 0%   B: 99%   C: 1%   D: 0%
Game 45. A: 2%   B: 95%   C: 1%   D: 2%
Game 46. A: 90%   B: 4%   C: 1%   D: 5%
Game 47. A: 0%   B: 0%   C: 97%   D: 3%
Game 48. A: 4%   B: 95%   C: 1%   D: 0%
Game 49. A: 0%   B: 1%   C: 99%   D: 0%
Game 50. A: 95%   B: 1%   C: 2%   D: 2%

£300

Game 1.   A: 98%   B: 2%   C: 0%   D: 0%
Game 2.   A: 10%   B: 95%   C: 4%   D: 1%
Game 3.   A: 1%   B: 1%   C: 98%   D: 0%
Game 4.   A: 93%   B: 2%   C: 5%   D: 0%
Game 5.   A: 95%   B: 0%   C: 5%   D: 0%
Game 6.   A: 90%   B: 5%   C: 5%   D: 0%
Game 7.   A: 85%   B: 10%   C: 5%   D: 0%
Game 8.   A: 5%   B: 10%   C: 81%   D: 4%
Game 9.   A: 0%   B: 5%   C: 5%   D: 95%
Game 10. A: 2%   B: 96%   C: 2%   D: 0%
Game 11. A: 3%   B: 1%   C: 1%   D: 95%
Game 12. A: 0%   B: 0%   C: 97%   D: 3%
Game 13. A: 0%   B: 0%   C: 2%   D: 97%
Game 14. A: 0%   B: 40%   C: 60%   D: 0%
Game 15. A: 15%   B: 4%   C: 2%   D: 79%
Game 16. A: 1%   B: 2%   C: 2%   D: 95%
Game 17. A: 0%   B: 1%   C: 0%   D: 99%
Game 18. A: 1%   B: 99%   C: 0%   D: 0%
Game 19. A: 0%   B: 10%   C: 3%   D: 87%
Game 20. A: 8%   B: 10%   C: 1%   D: 81%
Game 21. A: 1%   B: 0%   C: 4%   D: 95%
Game 22. A: 0%   B: 1%   C: 0%   D: 99%
Game 23. A: 0%   B: 4%   C: 95%   D: 1%
Game 24. A: 0%   B: 1%   C: 98%   D: 1%
Game 25. A: 99%   B: 0%   C: 1%   D: 0%
Game 26. A: 0%   B: 4%   C: 95%   D: 1%
Game 27. A: 5%   B: 90%   C: 1%   D: 4%
Game 28. A: 0%   B: 2%   C: 98%   D: 0%
Game 29. A: 1%   B: 5%   C: 4%   D: 90%
Game 30. A: 5%   B: 95%   C: 0%   D: 0%
Game 31. A: 95%   B: 0%   C: 5%   D: 0%
Game 32. A: 0%   B: 5%   C: 5%   D: 90%
Game 33. A: 5%   B: 0%   C: 90%   D: 5%
Game 34. A: 3%   B: 1%   C: 95%   D: 1%
Game 35. A: 5%   B: 10%   C: 75%   D: 10%
Game 36. A: 0%   B: 97%   C: 0%   D: 3%
Game 37. A: 1%   B: 0%   C: 99%   D: 0%
Game 38. A: 1%   B: 0%   C: 2%   D: 97%
Game 39. A: 1%   B: 95%   C: 2%   D: 2%
Game 40. A: 3%   B: 5%   C: 1%   D: 91%
Game 41. A: 3%   B: 90%   C: 4%   D: 3%
Game 42. A: 1%   B: 1%   C: 2%   D: 96%
Game 43. A: 15%   B: 5%   C: 5%   D: 80%
Game 44. A: 89%   B: 1%   C: 0%   D: 10%
Game 45. A: 3%   B: 90%   C: 4%   D: 3%
Game 46. A: 10%   B: 4%   C: 85%   D: 1%
Game 47. A: 5%   B: 0%   C: 0%   D: 95%
Game 48. A: 3%   B: 5%   C: 91%   D: 1%
Game 49. A: 1%   B: 90%   C: 4%   D: 5%
Game 50. A: 23%   B: 68%   C: 5%   D: 4%

£500

Game 1.   A: 85%   B: 4%   C: 1%   D: 10%
Game 2.   A: 1%   B: 99%   C: 0%   D: 0%
Game 3.   A: 5%   B: 0%   C: 95%   D: 0%
Game 4.   A: 0%   B: 0%   C: 1%   D: 99%
Game 5.   A: 0%   B: 0%   C: 97%   D: 3%
Game 6.   A: 3%   B: 95%   C: 1%   D: 1%
Game 7.   A: 0%   B: 10%   C: 87%   D: 3%
Game 8.   A: 95%   B: 1%   C: 4%   D: 0%
Game 9.   A: 5%   B: 91%   C: 0%   D: 4%
Game 10. A: 0%   B: 1%   C: 1%   D: 98%
Game 11. A: 15%   B: 5%   C: 2%   D: 78%
Game 12. A: 81%   B: 11%   C: 5%   D: 3%
Game 13. A: 95%   B: 0%   C: 1%   D: 4%
Game 14. A: 2%   B: 92%   C: 4%   D: 2%
Game 15. A: 0%   B: 90%   C: 2%   D: 8%
Game 16. A: 1%   B: 4%   C: 0%   D: 95%
Game 17. A: 1%   B: 81%   C: 8%   D: 10%
Game 18. A: 4%   B: 5%   C: 91%   D: 0%
Game 19. A: 4%   B: 90%   C: 4%   D: 2%
Game 20. A: 49%   B: 11%   C: 35%   D: 5%
Game 21. A: 14%   B: 35%   C: 31%   D: 20%
Game 22. A: 86%   B: 3%   C: 10%   D: 1%
Game 23. A: 8%   B: 72%   C: 12%   D: 8%
Game 24. A: 2%   B: 36%   C: 5%   D: 57%
Game 25. A: 10%   B: 87%   C: 3%   D: 0%
Game 26. A: 1%   B: 99%   C: 0%   D: 0%
Game 27. A: 78%   B: 13%   C: 5%   D: 4%
Game 28. A: 0%   B: 3%   C: 97%   D: 0%
Game 29. A: 6%   B: 25%   C: 1%   D: 68%
Game 30. A: 0%   B: 5%   C: 5%   D: 90%
Game 31. A: 8%   B: 50%   C: 38%   D: 4%
Game 32. A: 60%   B: 1%   C: 9%   D: 30%
Game 33. A: 0%   B: 1%   C: 99%   D: 0%
Game 34. A: 1%   B: 2%   C: 3%   D: 96%
Game 35. A: 5%   B: 80%   C: 5%   D: 10%
Game 36. A: 0%   B: 10%   C: 88%   D: 2%
Game 37. A: 3%   B: 5%   C: 0%   D: 92%
Game 38. A: 4%   B: 6%   C: 89%   D: 1%

Game 39. A: 0%   B: 98%   C: 1%   D: 1%
Game 40. A: 4%   B: 4%   C: 61%   D: 31%
Game 41. A: 3%   B: 97%   C: 0%   D: 0%
Game 42. A: 73%   B: 1%   C: 25%   D: 1%
Game 43. A: 23%   B: 1%   C: 70%   D: 6%
Game 44. A: 81%   B: 10%   C: 5%   D: 4%
Game 45. A: 28%   B: 2%   C: 68%   D: 2%
Game 46. A: 15%   B: 5%   C: 20%   D: 60%
Game 47. A: 3%   B: 3%   C: 4%   D: 90%
Game 48. A: 97%   B: 1%   C: 2%   D: 0%
Game 49. A: 5%   B: 3%   C: 91%   D: 1%
Game 50. A: 84%   B: 4%   C: 1 %   D: 10%

£1,000

Game 1. A: 15%   B: 2%   C: 43%   D: 40%
Game 2. A: 10%   B: 87 %   C: 3%   D: 0%
Game 3. A: 2%   B: 2%   C: 61%   D: 35%
Game 4. A: 5%   B: 1%   C: 94%   D: 0%
Game 5. A: 2%   B: 1%   C: 10%   D: 87%
Game 6. A: 3%   B: 2%   C: 10%   D: 85%
Game 7. A: 3%   B: 70%   C: 2%   D: 25%
Game 8. A: 0%   B: 0%   C: 98%   D: 2%
Game 9. A: 0%   B: 85%   C: 13%   D: 2%
Game 10. A: 65%   B: 5%   C: 25%   D: 5%
Game 11. A: 32%   B: 14%   C: 40%   D: 14%
Game 12. A: 89%   B: 6%   C: 3%   D: 2%
Game 13. A: 4%   B: 3%   C: 91%   D: 2%
Game 14. A: 3%   B: 2%   C: 0%   D: 95%
Game 15. A: 2%   B: 85%   C: 3%   D: 10%
Game 16. A: 3%   B: 90%   C: 4%   D: 3%
Game 17. A: 2%   B: 68%   C: 28%   D: 2%
Game 18. A: 1%   B: 12%   C: 1%   D: 85%
Game 19. A: 1%   B: 0%   C: 1%   D: 98%
Game 20. A: 32%   B: 14%   C: 16%   D: 38%
Game 21. A: 8%   B: 50%   C: 4%   D: 38%
Game 22. A: 89%   B: 3%   C: 2%   D: 6%
Game 23. A: 6%   B: 89%   C: 2%   D: 3%
Game 24. A: 72%   B: 8%   C: 12%   D: 8%
Game 25. A: 2%   B: 2%   C: 96%   D: 0%
Game 26. A: 57%   B: 2%   C: 5%   D: 36%
Game 27. A: 13%   B: 3%   C: 77%   D: 7%
Game 28. A: 8%   B: 20%   C: 17%   D: 55%
Game 29. A: 25%   B: 15%   C: 37%   D: 23%
Game 30. A: 19%   B: 11%   C: 9%   D: 61%
Game 31. A: 50%   B: 7%   C: 27%   D: 16%
Game 32. A: 12%   B: 76%   C: 11%   D: 1%
Game 33. A: 62%   B: 13%   C: 5%   D: 20%
Game 34. A: 12%   B: 2%   C: 46%   D: 40%
Game 35. A: 4%   B: 26%   C: 53%   D: 17%
Game 36. A: 89%   B: 4%   C: 2%   D: 5%
Game 37. A: 31%   B: 15%   C: 16%   D: 38%
Game 38. A: 59%   B: 5%   C: 15%   D: 21%
Game 39. A: 31%   B: 26%   C: 17%   D: 26%
Game 40. A: 97%   B: 2%   C: 1%   D: 0%
Game 41. A: 7%   B: 6%   C: 84%   D: 3%
Game 42. A: 9%   B: 13%   C: 42%   D: 36%
Game 43. A: 51%   B: 3%   C: 29%   D: 17%
Game 44. A: 1%   B: 4%   C: 89%   D: 6%
Game 45. A: 30%   B: 20%   C: 24%   D: 26%
Game 46. A: 5%   B: 64%   C: 21%   D: 10%
Game 47. A: 91%   B: 0%   C: 4%   D: 5%
Game 48. A: 22%   B: 97%   C: 9%   D: 2%
Game 49. A: 16 % B: 24%   C: 21 %   D: 39%
Game 50. A: 6%   B: 17%   C: 15%   D: 62%

£2000

Game 1. A: 12%   B: 47%   C: 12%   D: 29%
Game 2. A: 18%   B: 41%   C: 12%   D: 29%
Game 3. A: 37%   B: 10%   C: 46%   D: 7%
Game 4. A: 26%   B: 21%   C: 28%   D: 25%
Game 5. A: 7%   B: 26%   C: 52%   D: 15%
Game 6. A: 43%   B: 21%   C: 9%   D: 27%
Game 7. A: 39%   B: 4%   C: 27%   D: 30%
Game 8. A: 21%   B: 35%   C: 15%   D: 29%
Game 9. A: 17%   B: 23%   C: 19%   D: 41%
Game 10. A: 16%   B: 37%   C: 19%   D: 28%
Game 11. A: 20%   B: 17%   C: 61%   D: 2%
Game 12. A: 37%   B: 41%   C: 5%   D: 17%
Game 13. A: 25%   B: 27%   C: 29%   D: 19%
Game 14. A: 45%   B: 12%   C: 26%   D: 7%
Game 15. A: 41%   B: 15%   C: 26%   D: 18%
Game 16. A: 8%   B: 1%   C: 62%   D: 29%
Game 17. A: 31%   B: 64%   C: 3%   D: 2%
Game 18. A: 10%   B: 71%   C: 16%   D: 3%
Game 19. A: 25%   B: 29%   C: 37%   D: 9%
Game 20. A: 7%   B: 26%   C: 48%   D: 19%
Game 21. A: 28%   B: 16%   C: 45%   D: 11%
Game 22. A: 21%   B: 2%   C: 1%   D: 76%
Game 23. A: 16%   B: 27%   C: 35%   D: 22%
Game 24. A: 42%   B: 30%   C: 12%   D: 16%
Game 25. A: 12%   B: 17%   C: 68%   D: 3%
Game 26. A: 7%   B: 35%   C: 12%   D: 46%
Game 27. A: 21%   B: 18%   C: 22%   D: 39%
Game 28. A: 19%   B: 37%   C: 23%   D: 21%
Game 29. A: 26%   B: 41%   C: 20%   D: 13%
Game 30. A: 30%   B: 30%   C: 27%   D: 13%
Game 31. A: 10%   B: 46%   C: 38%   D: 6%
Game 32. A: 71%   B: 7%   C: 13%   D: 9%
Game 33. A: 51%   B: 25%   C: 13%   D: 11%
Game 34. A: 38%   B: 21%   C: 4%   D: 7%
Game 35. A: 31%   B: 21%   C: 29%   D: 19%
Game 36. A: 19%   B: 5%   C: 34%   D: 42%
Game 37. A: 38%   B: 34%   C: 16%   D: 12%
Game 38. A: 21%   B: 31%   C: 29%   D: 19%
Game 39. A: 21%   B: 45%   C: 19%   D: 15%
Game 40. A: 35%   B: 21%   C: 3%   D: 41%
Game 41. A: 5%   B: 31%   C: 38%   D: 26%
Game 42. A: 18%   B: 2%   C: 13%   D: 67%
Game 43. A: 9%   B: 21%   C: 68%   D: 2%
Game 44. A: 1%   B: 59%   C: 12%   D: 28%
Game 45. A: 17%   B: 37%   C: 30%   D: 46%
Game 46. A: 4%   B: 5%   C: 2%   D: 89%
Game 47. A: 59%   B: 24%   C: 7%   D: 10%
Game 48. A: 38%   B: 40%   C: 4%   D: 18%
Game 49. A: 34%   B: 37%   C: 21%   D: 8%
Game 50. A: 43%   B: 32%   C: 15%   D: 10%

£4,000

Game 1. A: 15%   B: 6%   C: 48%   D: 31%
Game 2. A: 7%   B: 8%   C: 14%   D: 71%
Game 3. A: 31%   B: 26%   C: 16%   D: 27%
Game 4. A: 35%   B: 12%   C: 39%   D: 14%
Game 5. A: 31%   B: 23%   C: 30%   D: 16%
Game 6. A: 31%   B: 16%   C: 21%   D: 32%
Game 7. A: 35%   B: 46%   C: 8%   D: 11%
Game 8. A: 5%   B: 61%   C: 8%   D: 26%
Game 9. A: 6%   B: 17%   C: 75%   D: 2%
Game 10. A: 10%   B: 9%   C: 46%   D: 35%
Game 11. A: 25%   B: 15%   C: 37%   D: 23%
Game 12. A: 2%   B: 5%   C: 4%   D: 89%

Game 13. A: 27%   B: 7%   C: 16%   D: 50%
Game 14. A: 5%   B: 4%   C: 2%   D: 89%
Game 15. A: 15%   B: 5%   C: 21%   D: 59%
Game 16. A: 10%   B: 26%   C: 27%   D: 37%
Game 17. A: 16%   B: 24%   C: 39%   D: 21%
Game 18. A: 9%   B: 21%   C: 43%   D: 27%
Game 19. A: 52%   B: 26%   C: 7%   D: 15%
Game 20. A: 61%   B: 17%   C: 20%   D: 2%
Game 21. A: 37%   B: 41%   C: 5%   D: 17%
Game 22. A: 16%   B: 28%   C: 37%   D: 19%
Game 23. A: 8%   B: 1%   C: 62%   D: 29%
Game 24. A: 9%   B: 37%   C: 29%   D: 25%
Game 25. A: 27%   B: 35%   C: 22%   D: 16%
Game 26. A: 7%   B: 46%   C: 12%   D: 35%
Game 27. A: 26%   B: 41%   C: 20%   D: 13%
Game 28. A: 19%   B: 11%   C: 9%   D: 61%
Game 29. A: 17%   B: 9%   C: 55%   D: 19%
Game 30. A: 14%   B: 11%   C: 32%   D: 43%
Game 31. A: 61%   B: 11%   C: 9%   D: 19%
Game 32. A: 14%   B: 32%   C: 11%   D: 43%
Game 33. A: 22%   B: 67%   C: 9%   D: 2%
Game 34. A: 11%   B: 46%   C: 24%   D: 19%
Game 35. A: 21%   B: 61%   C: 3%   D: 15%
Game 36. A: 19%   B: 31%   C: 24%   D: 26%
Game 37. A: 34%   B: 26%   C: 31%   D: 9%
Game 38. A: 25%   B: 31%   C: 19%   D: 25%
Game 39. A: 29%   B: 25 %   C: 26%   D: 20%
Game 40. A: 24%   B: 14%   C: 25%   D: 37%
Game 41. A: 28%   B: 18%   C: 22 %   D: 32%
Game 42. A: 6%   B: 20%   C: 27%   D: 47%
Game 43. A: 27%   B: 20%   C: 35%   D: 18%
Game 44. A: 19%   B: 27%   C: 26%   D: 28%
Game 45. A: 39%   B: 4%   C: 51%   D: 6%
Game 46. A: 27%   B: 41%   C: 15%   D: 17%
Game 47. A: 26%   B: 11%   C: 24%   D: 39%
Game 48. A: 37%   B: 40%   C: 7%   D: 16%
Game 49. A: 11 % B: 41%   C: 29%   D: 19%
Game 50. A: 45%   B: 17 %   C: 31%   D: 7%

£8,000

Game 1. A: 19%   B: 34%   C: 22%   D: 25%
Game 2. A: 14%   B: 25%   C: 36%   D: 25%
Game 3. A: 3%   B: 65%   C: 21%   D: 11%
Game 4. A: 10%   B: 47%   C: 28%   D: 15%
Game 5. A: 25%   B: 9%   C: 1%   D: 65%
Game 6. A: 1%   B: 67%   C: 29%   D: 3%
Game 7. A: 28%   B: 48%   C: 5%   D: 19%
Game 8. A: 38%   B: 17%   C: 1%   D: 44%
Game 9. A: 22%   B: 52%   C: 19%   D: 7%
Game 10. A: 47%   B: 23%   C: 11%   D: 19%
Game 11. A: 24%   B: 12%   C: 27%   D: 37%
Game 12. A: 27%   B: 19%   C: 19%   D: 35%
Game 13. A: 27%   B: 31%   C: 1%   D: 41%
Game 14. A: 23%   B: 24%   C: 17%   D: 34%
Game 15. A: 22%   B: 31%   C: 29%   D: 18%
Game 16. A: 27%   B: 19%   C: 23%   D: 29%
Game 17. A: 19%   B: 27%   C: 38%   D: 16%
Game 18. A: 24%   B: 26%   C: 27%   D: 23%
Game 19. A: 47%   B: 17%   C: 28%   D: 8%
Game 20. A: 21%   B: 27%   C: 43%   D: 9%
Game 21. A: 41%   B: 30%   C: 22%   D: 7%
Game 22. A: 25%   B: 28%   C: 20%   D: 27%
Game 23. A: 34%   B: 15%   C: 20%   D: 31%
Game 24. A: 24%   B: 16%   C: 29%   D: 31%
Game 25. A: 16%   B: 41%   C: 42%   D: 1%

Game 26. A: 23%   B: 10%   C: 38%   D: 19%
Game 27. A: 10%   B: 67%   C: 2%   D: 21%
Game 28. A: 37%   B: 24%   C: 30%   D: 9%
Game 29. A: 29%   B: 23%   C: 25%   D: 23%
Game 30. A: 41%   B: 32%   C: 10%   D: 17%
Game 31. A: 11%   B: 21%   C: 61%   D: 7%
Game 32. A: 31%   B: 38%   C: 10%   D: 21%
Game 33. A: 21%   B: 30%   C: 25%   D: 24%
Game 34. A: 10%   B: 21%   C: 54%   D: 15%
Game 35. A: 81%   B: 1%   C: 11%   D: 7%
Game 36. A: 25%   B: 8%   C: 61%   D: 6%
Game 37. A: 24%   B: 17%   C: 39%   D: 20%
Game 38. A: 30%   B: 33%   C: 31%   D: 6%
Game 39. A: 14%   B: 5%   C: 72%   D: 9%
Game 40. A: 25%   B: 13%   C: 11%   D: 51%
Game 41. A: 22%   B: 26%   C: 24%   D: 28%
Game 42. A: 23%   B: 3%   C: 7%   D: 67%
Game 43. A: 21%   B: 3%   C: 61%   D: 15%
Game 44. A: 46%   B: 11%   C: 24%   D: 19%
Game 45. A: 9%   B: 22%   C: 97%   D: 2%
Game 46. A: 43%   B: 11%   C: 32%   D: 14%
Game 47. A: 9%   B: 19%   C: 11%   D: 61%
Game 48. A: 19%   B: 17%   C: 9%   D: 55%
Game 49. A: 61%   B:11%   C:9%   D: 19%
Game 50. A: 26%   B: 20%   C: 41%   D: 13%

£16,000
Game 1. A: 7%   B: 46%   C: 35%   D: 12%
Game 2. A: 27%   B: 22%   C: 16%   D: 35%
Game 3. A: 14%   B: 11%   C: 32%   D: 43%
Game 4. A: 15%   B: 61%   C: 21%   D: 3%
Game 5. A: 19%   B: 24%   C: 46%   D: 11%
Game 6. A: 22%   B: 67%   C: 9%   D: 2%
Game 7. A: 32%   B: 43%   C: 11%   D: 14%
Game 8. A: 19%   B: 61%   C: 11%   D: 9%
Game 9. A: 15%   B: 52%   C: 7%   D: 26%
Game 10. A: 9%   B: 29%   C: 23%   D: 37%
Game 11. A: 8%   B: 1%   C: 29%   D: 62%
Game 12. A: 16%   B: 37%   C: 28%   D: 19%
Game 13. A: 17%   B: 5%   C: 37%   D: 41%
Game 14. A: 20%   B: 61%   C: 17%   D: 2%
Game 15. A: 43%   B: 21%   C: 27%   D: 9%
Game 16. A: 16%   B: 24%   C: 39%   D: 21%
Game 17. A: 26%   B: 10%   C: 37%   D: 27%
Game 18. A: 21%   B: 3%   C: 15%   D: 59%
Game 19. A: 51%   B: 13%   C: 25%   D: 11%
Game 20. A: 4%   B: 68%   C: 7%   D: 21%
Game 21. A: 27%   B: 7%   C: 50%   D: 16%
Game 22. A: 89%   B: 5%   C: 4%   D: 2%
Game 23. A: 25%   B: 15%   C: 23%   D: 37%
Game 24. A: 35%   B: 10%   C: 46%   D: 9%
Game 25. A: 6%   B: 2%   C: 17%   D: 75%
Game 26. A: 26%   B: 61%   C: 5%   D: 8%
Game 27. A: 8%   B: 46%   C: 35%   D: 11%
Game 28. A: 21%   B: 16%   C: 32%   D: 31%
Game 29. A: 30%   B: 23%   C: 16%   D: 31%
Game 30. A: 35%   B: 39%   C: 12%   D: 14%
Game 31. A: 16%   B: 31%   C: 26%   D:27%
Game 32. A: 7%   B: 8%   C: 71%   D: 14%
Game 33. A: 15%   B: 31%   C: 48%   D: 6%
Game 34. A: 25%   B: 43%   C: 2%   D: 30%
Game 35. A: 21%   B: 37%   C: 34%   D: 8%
Game 36. A: 37%   B: 6%   C: 39%   D: 18%
Game 37. A: 24%   B: 7%   C: 10%   D: 59%
Game 38. A: 4%   B: 89%   C: 2%   D: 5%

Game 39. A: 37%   B: 46%   C: 0%   D: 17%
Game 40. A: 1%   B: 12%   C: 28%   D: 59%
Game 41. A: 21%   B: 68%   C: 2%   D: 9%
Game 42. A: 67%   B: 2%   C: 18%   D: 13%
Game 43. A: 31%   B: 5%   C: 38%   D: 26%
Game 44. A: 41%   B: 21%   C: 35%   D: 3%
Game 45. A: 45%   B: 19%   C: 15%   D: 21%
Game 46. A: 38%   B: 12%   C: 16%   D: 34%
Game 47. A: 19%   B: 34%   C: 5%   D: 42%
Game 48. A: 10%   B: 38%   C: 6%   D: 46%
Game 49. A: 31%   B: 23%   C: 22%   D: 24%
Game 50. A: 21%   B: 19%   C: 37%   D: 23%

£32,000
Game 1. A:27%   B: 30%   C: 22%   D: 21%
Game 2. A: 30%   B: 37%   C: 21%   D: 12%
Game 3. A: 29%   B: 19%   C: 38%   D: 14%
Game 4. A: 19%   B: 22%   C: 30%   D: 29%
Game 5. A: 14%   B: 72%   C: 5%   D: 9%
Game 6. A: 31%   B:30%   C: 33%   D: 6%
Game 7. A: 24%   B: 39%   C: 17%   D: 20%
Game 8. A: 24%   B: 22%   C: 28%   D: 26%
Game 9. A: 3%   B: 67%   C: 7%   D: 23%
Game 10. A: 8%   B: 25%   C: 61%   D: 6%
Game 11. A: 7%   B: 11%   C: 81%   D: 1%
Game 12. A: 15%   B: 10%   C: 54%   D: 21%
Game 13. A: 21%   B: 30%   C: 25%   D: 24%
Game 14. A: 21%   B: 10%   C: 38%   D: 31%
Game 15. A: 7%   B: 21%   C: 11%   D: 61%
Game 16. A: 10%   B: 32%   C: 17%   D: 41%
Game 17. A: 25%   B: 23%   C: 23%   D: 29%
Game 18. A: 30%   B: 24%   C: 37%   D: 9%
Game 19. A: 7%   B: 20%   C: 24%   D: 29%
Game 20. A: 10%   B: 21%   C: 2%   D: 67%
Game 21. A: 38%   B: 23%   C: 19%   D: 10%
Game 22. A: 29%   B: 21%   C: 23%   D: 27%
Game 23. A: 16%   B: 41%   C: 42%   D: 1%
Game 24. A: 16%   B: 31%   C: 24%   D: 29%
Game 25. A: 15%   B: 20%   C: 34%   D: 31%
Game 26. A: 27%   B: 25%   C: 28%   D: 20%
Game 27. A: 30%   B: 7%   C: 41%   D: 22%
Game 28. A: 27%   B: 9%   C: 43%   D: 21%
Game 29. A: 28%   B: 17%   C: 47%   D: 8%
Game 30. A: 24%   B: 23%   C: 26%   D: 27%
Game 31. A: 38%   B: 27%   C: 19%   D: 16%
Game 32. A: 29%   B: 25%   C: 27%   D: 19%
Game 33. A: 22%   B: 18%   C: 29%   D: 31%
Game 34. A: 25%   B: 17%   C: 24%   D: 34%
Game 35. A: 27%   B: 41%   C: 1%   D: 31%
Game 36. A: 27%   B: 19%   C: 19%   D: 35%
Game 37. A: 37%   B: 24%   C: 27%   D: 12%
Game 38. A: 23%   B: 47%   C: 11%   D: 19%
Game 39. A: 30%   B: 11%   C: 47%   D: 6%
Game 40. A: 19%   B: 25%   C: 22%   D: 34%
Game 41. A: 17%   B: 31%   C: 45%   D: 7%
Game 42. A: 29%   B: 19%   C: 11%   D: 41%
Game 43. A: 7%   B: 37%   C: 40%   D: 16%
Game 44. A: 26%   B: 11%   C: 39%   D: 24%
Game 45. A: 17%   B: 27%   C: 41%   D: 15%
Game 46. A: 51%   B: 4%   C: 6%   D: 39%
Game 47. A: 19%   B: 27%   C: 28%   D: 26%
Game 48. A: 20%   B: 27%   C: 35%   D: 18%
Game 49. A: 6%   B: 27%   C: 47%   D: 20%
Game 50. A: 25%   B: 14%   C: 24%   D: 37%

£64,000
Game 1. A: 25%   B: 20%   C: 29%   D: 26%
Game 2. A: 25%   B: 31%   C: 25%   D: 19%
Game 3. A: 26%   B: 31%   C: 9%   D: 34%
Game 4. A: 24%   B: 19%   C: 26%   D: 31%
Game 5. A: 44%   B: 28%   C: 1%   D: 27%
Game 6. A: 26%   B: 44%   C: 15%   D: 15%
Game 7. A: 18%   B: 1%   C: 62%   D: 19%
Game 8. A: 68%   B: 5%   C: 20%   D: 7%
Game 9. A: 23%   B: 14%   C: 12%   D: 51%
Game 10. A: 4%   B: 34%   C: 32%   D: 30%
Game 11. A: 17%   B: 31%   C: 44%   D: 8%
Game 12. A: 53%   B: 34%   C: 13%   D: 0%
Game 13. A: 1%   B: 22%   C: 11%   D: 66%
Game 14. A: 25%   B: 60%   C: 3%   D: 12%
Game 15. A: 4%   B: 59%   C: 37%   D: 0%
Game 16. A: 36%   B: 40%   C: 20%   D: 4%
Game 17. A: 14%   B: 46%   C: 35%   D: 5%
Game 18. A: 18%   B: 5%   C: 37%   D: 40%
Game 19. A: 30%   B: 40%   C: 22%   D: 8%
Game 20. A: 44%   B: 28%   C: 1%   D: 27%
Game 21. A: 34%   B: 5%   C: 45%   D: 16%
Game 22. A: 1%   B: 44%   C: 1%   D: 54%
Game 23. A: 44%   B: 21%   C: 28%   D: 7%
Game 24. A: 55%   B: 16%   C: 26%   D: 3%
Game 25. A: 56%   B: 42%   C: 1%   D: 1%
Game 26. A: 30%   B: 23%   C: 5%   D: 42%
Game 27. A: 25%   B: 14%   C: 24%   D: 37%
Game 28. A: 62%   B: 6%   C: 14%   D: 18%
Game 29. A: 34%   B: 16%   C: 5%   D: 45%
Game 30. A: 5%   B: 68%   C: 20%   D: 7%
Game 31. A: 11%   B: 11%   C: 45%   D: 33%
Game 32. A: 3%   B: 12%   C: 31%   D: 54%
Game 33. A: 32%   B: 33%   C: 24%   D: 11%
Game 34. A: 53%   B: 9%   C: 2%   D: 36%
Game 35. A: 25%   B: 37%   C: 22%   D: 16%
Game 36. A: 30%   B: 42%   C: 23%   D: 5%
Game 37. A: 2%   B: 3%   C: 53%   D: 42%
Game 38. A: 38%   B: 48%   C: 13%   D: 1%
Game 39. A: 10%   B: 10%   C: 25%   D: 55%
Game 40. A: 17%   B: 38%   C: 1%   D: 44%
Game 41. A: 16%   B: 3%   C: 55%   D: 26%
Game 42. A: 45%   B: 34%   C: 16%   D: 5%
Game 43. A: 17%   B: 33%   C: 49%   D: 1%
Game 44. A: 32%   B: 33%   C: 24%   D: 11%
Game 45. A: 13%   B: 39%   C: 2%   D: 46%
Game 46. A: 40%   B: 36%   C: 4%   D: 20%
Game 47. A: 40%   B: 32%   C: 19%   D: 9%
Game 48. A: 21%   B: 56%   C: 12%   D: 11%
Game 49. A: 7%   B: 30%   C: 11%   D: 52%
Game 50. A: 4%   B: 21%   C: 22%   D: 53%

£125,000
Game 1. A: 21%   B: 11%   C: 56%   D: 12%
Game 2. A: 30%   B: 9%   C: 6%   D: 55%
Game 3. A: 4%   B: 21%   C: 22%   D: 53%
Game 4. A: 63%   B: 6%   C: 8%   D: 23%
Game 5. A: 28%   B: 30%   C: 32%   D: 10%
Game 6. A: 58%   B: 11%   C: 26%   D: 5%
Game 7. A: 33%   B: 46%   C: 19%   D: 2%
Game 8. A: 3%   B: 54%   C: 31%   D: 12%
Game 9. A: 18%   B: 6%   C: 14%   D: 62%
Game 10. A: 5%   B: 34%   C: 45%   D: 16%
Game 11. A: 37%   B: 45%   C 12:%   D: 6%
Game 12. A: 26%   B: 29%   C: 25%   D: 20%

Game 13. A: 4%   B: 51%   C: 39%   D: 6%
Game 14. A: 26%   B: 39%   C: 24%   D: 11%
Game 15. A: 28%   B: 27%   C: 26%   D: 19%
Game 16. A: 37%   B: 27%   C: 12%   D: 24%
Game 17. A: 27%   B: 35%   C: 19%   D: 19%
Game 18. A: 28%   B: 17%   C: 47%   D: 8%
Game 19. A: 19%   B: 38%   C: 16%   D: 27%
Game 20. A: 16%   B: 41%   C: 1%   D: 42%
Game 21. A: 21%   B: 27%   C: 43%   D: 9%
Game 22. A: 32%   B: 41%   C: 10%   D: 17%
Game 23. A: 31%   B: 38%   C: 10%   D: 21%
Game 24. A: 21%   B: 24%   C: 25%   D: 30%
Game 25. A: 37%   B: 14%   C: 25%   D: 24%
Game 26. A: 31%   B: 26%   C: 34%   D: 9%
Game 27. A: 14%   B: 25%   C: 36%   D: 25%
Game 28. A: 44%   B: 17%   C: 38%   D: 1%
Game 29. A: 27%   B: 19%   C: 29%   D: 23%
Game 30. A: 23%   B: 27%   C: 26%   D: 24%
Game 31. A: 22%   B: 29%   C: 31%   D: 18%
Game 32. A:10%   B: 49%   C: 34%   D: 7%
Game 33. A: 23%   B: 14%   C: 12%   D: 51%
Game 34. A: 34%   B: 45%   C: 5%   D: 16%
Game 35. A: 10%   B: 46%   C: 12%   D: 32%
Game 36. A: 26%   B: 34%   C: 30%   D: 10%
Game 37. A: 4%   B: 34%   C: 46%   D: 16%
Game 38. A: 6%   B: 63%   C: 9%   D: 22%
Game 39. A: 22%   B: 53%   C: 21%   D: 4%
Game 40. A: 14%   B: 46%   C: 35%   D: 5%
Game 41. A: 34%   B: 5%   C: 45%   D: 16%
Game 42. A: 5%   B: 68%   C: 20%   D: 7%
Game 43. A: 12%   B: 20%   C: 34%   D: 34%
Game 44. A: 17%   B: 31%   C: 8%   D: 44%
Game 45. A: 0%   B: 73%   C: 4%   D: 23%
Game 46. A: 27%   B: 41%   C: 15%   D: 17%
Game 47. A: 22%   B: 19%   C: 7%   D: 52%
Game 48. A: 24%   B: 27%   C: 37%   D: 12%
Game 49. A: 28%   B: 17%   C: 47%   D: 8%
Game 50. A: 17%   B: 37%   C: 19%   D: 27%

£250,000
Game 1. A: 23%   B: 23%   C: 28%   D: 26%
Game 2. A: 21%   B: 27%   C: 43%   D: 9%
Game 3. A: 23%   B: 29%   C: 16%   D: 32%
Game 4. A: 15%   B: 40%   C: 43%   D: 2%
Game 5. A: 25%   B: 51%   C: 13%   D: 11%
Game 6. A: 24%   B: 39%   C: 17%   D: 20%
Game 7. A: 27%   B: 14%   C: 15%   D: 44%
Game 8. A: 2%   B: 67%   C: 10%   D: 21%
Game 9. A: 20%   B: 30%   C: 45%   D: 5%
Game 10. A: 28%   B: 7%   C: 44%   D: 21%
Game 11. A: 2%   B: 42%   C: 3%   D: 53%
Game 12. A: 6%   B: 21%   C: 10%   D: 63%
Game 13. A: 29%   B: 56%   C: 6%   D: 9%
Game 14. A: 22%   B: 10%   C: 56%   D: 12%
Game 15. A: 33%   B: 1%   C: 46%   D: 20%
Game 16. A: 10%   B: 60%   C: 24%   D: 6%
Game 17. A: 29%   B: 48%   C: 5%   D: 18%
Game 18. A: 18%   B: 62%   C: 14%   D: 6%
Game 19. A: 23%   B: 30%   C: 5%   D: 42%
Game 20. A: 24%   B: 5%   C: 61%   D: 10%
Game 21. A: 45%   B: 16%   C: 5%   D: 34%
Game 22. A: 7%   B: 41%   C: 2%   D: 50%
Game 23. A: 60%   B: 30%   C: 6%   D: 4%
Game 24. A: 24%   B: 37%   C: 25%   D: 14%
Game 25. A: 44%   B: 27%   C: 19%   D: 10%

Game 26. A: 7%   B: 18%   C: 69%   D: 6%
Game 27. A: 54%   B: 21%   C: 8%   D: 17%
Game 28. A: 13%   B: 16%   C: 60%   D: 11%
Game 29. A: 15%   B: 37%   C: 37%   D: 11%
Game 30. A: 45%   B: 6%   C: 37%   D: 12%
Game 31. A: 49%   B: 44%   C: 1%   D: 6%
Game 32. A: 35%   B: 13%   C: 49%   D: 3%
Game 33. A: 21%   B: 44%   C: 28%   D: 7%
Game 34. A: 17%   B: 44%   C: 24%   D: 15%
Game 35. A: 35%   B: 5%   C: 14%   D: 46%
Game 36. A: 22%   B: 26%   C: 36%   D: 16%
Game 37. A: 27%   B: 34%   C: 11%   D: 28%
Game 38. A: 4%   B: 50%   C: 2%   D: 44%
Game 39. A: 9%   B: 8%   C: 49%   D: 34%
Game 40. A: 22%   B: 29%   C: 27%   D: 22%
Game 41. A: 29%   B: 38%   C: 14%   D: 19%
Game 42. A: 22%   B: 24%   C: 28%   D: 26%
Game 43. A: 31%   B: 33%   C: 6%   D: 30%
Game 44. A: 10%   B: 54%   C: 15%   D: 21%
Game 45. A: 32%   B: 10%   C: 41%   D: 17%
Game 46. A: 23%   B: 10%   C: 38%   D: 19%
Game 47. A: 16%   B: 42%   C: 41%   D: 11%
Game 48. A: 27%   B: 25%   C: 28%   D: 20%
Game 49. A: 34%   B: 15%   C: 20%   D: 31%
Game 50. A: 24%   B: 37%   C: 27%   D: 12%

£500,000
Game 1. A: 27%   B: 19%   C: 19%   D: 35%
Game 2. A: 25%   B: 25%   C: 34%   D: 16%
Game 3. A: 19%   B: 11%   C: 29%   D: 41%
Game 4. A: 19%   B: 22%   C: 25%   D: 34%
Game 5. A: 7%   B: 40%   C: 16%   D: 37%
Game 6. A: 61%   B: 25%   C: 0%   D: 14%
Game 7. A: 6%   B: 47%   C: 27%   D: 20%
Game 8. A: 51%   B: 39%   C: 6%   D: 4%
Game 9. A: 14%   B: 37%   C: 24%   D: 25%
Game 10. A: 26%   B: 31%   C: 34%   D: 9%
Game 11. A: 31%   B: 25%   C: 25%   D: 19%
Game 12. A: 25%   B: 23%   C: 15%   D: 37%
Game 13. A: 31%   B: 34%   C: 10%   D: 25%
Game 14. A: 1%   B: 67%   C: 3%   D: 29%
Game 15. A: 11%   B: 3%   C: 21%   D: 65%
Game 16. A: 16%   B: 2%   C: 44%   D: 38%
Game 17. A: 42%   B: 16%   C: 41%   D: 1%
Game 18. A: 9%   B: 27%   C: 21%   D: 43%
Game 19. A: 24%   B: 37%   C: 30%   D: 9%
Game 20. A: 41%   B: 32%   C: 10%   D: 17%
Game 21. A: 25%   B: 8%   C: 61%   D: 6%
Game 22. A: 54%   B: 21%   C: 10%   D: 15%
Game 23. A: 40%   B: 18%   C: 32%   D: 10%
Game 24. A: 49%   B: 3%   C: 27%   D: 21%
Game 25. A: 18%   B: 62%   C: 5%   D: 15%
Game 26. A: 32%   B: 41%   C: 16%   D: 11%
Game 27. A: 27%   B: 60%   C: 7%   D: 6%
Game 28. A: 21%   B: 25%   C: 38%   D: 16%
Game 29. A: 29%   B: 19%   C: 21%   D: 31%
Game 30. A: 14%   B: 24%   C: 45%   D: 17%
Game 31. A: 12%   B: 15%   C: 34%   D: 39%
Game 32. A: 43%   B: 10%   C: 21%   D: 26%
Game 33. A: 50%   B: 17%   C: 25%   D: 8%
Game 34. A: 41%   B: 56%   C: 3%   D: 0%
Game 35. A: 14%   B: 11%   C: 32%   D: 43%
Game 36. A: 16%   B: 31%   C: 38%   D: 15%
Game 37. A: 43%   B: 9%   C: 13%   D: 36%
Game 38. A: 7%   B: 3%   C: 6%   D: 84%

Game 39. A: 16%   B: 24%   C: 39%   D: 21%
Game 40. A: 22%   B: 67%   C: 9%   D: 2%
Game 41. A: 12%   B: 13%   C: 47%   D: 28%
Game 42. A: 5%   B: 37%   C: 46%   D: 12%
Game 43. A: 21%   B: 15%   C: 28%   D: 36%
Game 44. A: 30%   B: 16%   C: 37%   D: 27%
Game 45. A: 21%   B: 26%   C: 46%   D: 7%
Game 46. A: 8%   B: 1%   C: 29%   D: 62%
Game 47. A: 29%   B: 25%   C: 27%   D: 19%
Game 48. A: 16%   B: 10%   C: 71%   D: 3%
Game 49. A: 37%   B: 21%   C: 23%   D: 19%
Game 50. A: 9%   B: 17%   C: 55%   D: 19%

£1,000,000
Game 1.   A: 25%   B: 15%   C: 23%   D: 37%
Game 2.   A: 8%   B: 1%   C: 49%   D: 42%
Game 3.   A: 24%   B: 37%   C: 24%   D: 15%
Game 4.   A: 61%   B: 29%   C: 5%   D: 5%
Game 5.   A: 7%   B: 19%   C: 69%   D: 5%
Game 6.   A: 50%   B: 45%   C: 7%   D: 0%
Game 7.   A: 11%   B: 16%   C: 13%   D: 60%
Game 8.   A: 44%   B: 0%   C: 12%   D: 44%
Game 9.   A: 24%   B: 28%   C: 22%   D: 26%
Game 10. A: 14%   B: 29%   C: 38%   D: 19%
Game 11. A: 20%   B: 15%   C: 34%   D: 31%
Game 12. A: 16%   B: 40%   C: 8%   D: 36%
Game 13. A: 33%   B: 20%   C: 26%   D: 21%
Game 14. A: 23%   B: 43%   C: 30%   D: 4%
Game 15. A: 18%   B: 62%   C: 15%   D: 5%
Game 16. A: 25%   B: 34%   C: 32%   D: 9%
Game 17. A: 5%   B: 5%   C: 40%   D: 50%
Game 18. A: 14%   B: 25%   C: 36%   D: 25%
Game 19. A: 10%   B: 28%   C: 47%   D: 15%
Game 20. A: 24%   B: 27%   C: 23%   D: 26%
Game 21. A: 25%   B: 23%   C: 29%   D: 23%
Game 22. A: 10%   B: 2%   C: 61%   D: 21%
Game 23. A: 38%   B: 23%   C: 10%   D: 19%
Game 24. A: 24%   B: 5%   C: 61%   D: 10%
Game 25. A: 25%   B: 24%   C: 39%   D: 11%
Game 26. A: 4%   B: 51%   C: 6%   D: 39%
Game 27. A: 30%   B: 12%   C: 37%   D: 21%
Game 28. A: 14%   B: 44%   C:15%   D: 27%
Game 29. A: 20%   B: 3%   C: 37%   D: 40%
Game 30. A: 36%   B: 13%   C: 33%   D: 18%
Game 31. A: 30%   B: 33%   C: 42%   D: 5%
Game 32. A: 45%   B: 16%   C: 5%   D: 34%
Game 33. A: 32%   B: 19%   C: 8%   D: 41%
Game 34. A: 28%   B: 10%   C: 31%   D: 31%
Game 35. A: 19%   B: 22%   C: 30%   D: 29%
Game 36. A: 30%   B: 12%   C: 21%   D: 37%
Game 37. A: 24%   B: 20%   C: 17%   D: 39%
Game 38. A: 21%   B: 38%   C: 31%   D: 10%
Game 39. A: 29%   B: 38%   C: 20%   D: 13%
Game 40. A: 7%   B: 61%   C: 11%   D: 21%
Game 41. A: 16%   B: 31%   C: 24%   D: 29%
Game 42. A: 16%   B: 41%   C: 42%   D: 1%
Game 43. A: 24%   B: 26%   C: 27%   D: 23%
Game 44. A: 43%   B: 9%   C: 27%   D: 21%
Game 45. A: 29%   B: 24%   C: 27%   D: 20%
Game 46. A: 23%   B: 11%   C: 47%   D: 19%
Game 47. A: 30%   B: 22%   C: 40%   D: 8%
Game 48. A: 23%   B: 26%   C: 27%   D: 24%
Game 49. A: 10%   B: 28%   C: 32%   D: 30%
Game 50. A: 24%   B: 5%   C: 61%   D: 10%

ANSWERS

Game 1

£100	C	£200	D	£300	A
£500	A	£1,000	C	£2,000	B
£4,000	C	£8,000	B	£16,000	B
£32,000	B	£64,000	C	£125,000	C
£250,000	C	£500,000	D	£1,000,000	D

Game 2

£100	B	£200	B	£300	B
£500	B	£1,000	B	£2,000	B
£4,000	D	£8,000	C	£16,000	D
£32,000	B	£64,000	B	£125,000	D
£250,000	C	£500,000	C	£1,000,000	C

Game 3

£100	B	£200	C	£300	C
£500	C	£1,000	C	£2,000	C
£4,000	A	£8,000	B	£16,000	C
£32,000	C	£64,000	D	£125,000	D
£250,000	D	£500,000	D	£1,000,000	B

Game 4

£100	C	£200	B	£300	A
£500	D	£1,000	C	£2,000	C
£4,000	C	£8,000	B	£16,000	B
£32,000	C	£64,000	D	£125,000	A
£250,000	C	£500,000	D	£1,000,000	A

Game 5

£100	B	£200	B	£300	A
£500	C	£1,000	D	£2,000	C
£4,000	A	£8,000	D	£16,000	C
£32,000	A	£64,000	A	£125,000	C
£250,000	B	£500,000	B	£1,000,000	C

Game 6

£100	A	£200	C	£300	A
£500	B	£1,000	D	£2,000	A
£4,000	D	£8,000	B	£16,000	B
£32,000	D	£64,000	B	£125,000	A
£250,000	B	£500,000	A	£1,000,000	A

Game 7

£100	A	£200	B	£300	A
£500	C	£1,000	B	£2,000	A
£4,000	B	£8,000	B	£16,000	B
£32,000	B	£64,000	C	£125,000	B
£250,000	D	£500,000	B	£1,000,000	D

Game 8

£100	C	£200	A	£300	C
£500	A	£1,000	C	£2,000	D
£4,000	B	£8,000	D	£16,000	B
£32,000	C	£64,000	A	£125,000	B
£250,000	B	£500,000	A	£1,000,000	C

Game 9

£100	C	£200	B	£300	D
£500	B	£1,000	B	£2,000	B
£4,000	D	£8,000	B	£16,000	B
£32,000	B	£64,000	D	£125,000	D
£250,000	C	£500,000	B	£1,000,000	B

Game 10

£100	B	£200	C	£300	B
£500	D	£1,000	A	£2,000	B
£4,000	C	£8,000	A	£16,000	D
£32,000	C	£64,000	B	£125,000	C
£250,000	C	£500,000	C	£1,000,000	C

ANSWERS

Game 11

£100	C	£200	B	£300	D
£500	D	£1,000	C	£2,000	C
£4,000	C	£8,000	C	£16,000	D
£32,000	C	£64,000	C	£125,000	B
£250,000	D	£500,000	A	£1,000,000	C

Game 12

£100	C	£200	D	£300	C
£500	A	£1,000	A	£2,000	B
£4,000	D	£8,000	D	£16,000	B
£32,000	B	£64,000	A	£125,000	B
£250,000	D	£500,000	D	£1,000,000	B

Game 13

£100	B	£200	C	£300	D
£500	A	£1,000	C	£2,000	C
£4,000	D	£8,000	D	£16,000	D
£32,000	B	£64,000	D	£125,000	B
£250,000	B	£500,000	B	£1,000,000	A

Game 14

£100	D	£200	D	£300	C
£500	B	£1,000	D	£2,000	A
£4,000	D	£8,000	D	£16,000	B
£32,000	C	£64,000	B	£125,000	A
£250,000	C	£500,000	B	£1,000,000	B

Game 15

£100	D	£200	D	£300	D
£500	B	£1,000	B	£2,000	A
£4,000	D	£8,000	B	£16,000	A
£32,000	D	£64,000	B	£125,000	A
£250,000	C	£500,000	D	£1,000,000	B

Game 16

£100	B	£200	A	£300	D
£500	D	£1,000	B	£2,000	C
£4,000	D	£8,000	D	£16,000	C
£32,000	D	£64,000	B	£125,000	A
£250,000	B	£500,000	C	£1,000,000	B

Game 17

£100	A	£200	C	£300	D
£500	B	£1,000	D	£2,000	B
£4,000	C	£8,000	C	£16,000	C
£32,000	D	£64,000	B	£125,000	B
£250,000	B	£500,000	A	£1,000,000	D

Game 18

£100	C	£200	C	£300	B
£500	C	£1,000	D	£2,000	B
£4,000	C	£8,000	D	£16,000	D
£32,000	C	£64,000	D	£125,000	C
£250,000	B	£500,000	D	£1,000,000	C

Game 19

£100	B	£200	D	£300	D
£500	B	£1,000	D	£2,000	C
£4,000	A	£8,000	A	£16,000	A
£32,000	D	£64,000	B	£125,000	B
£250,000	D	£500,000	B	£1,000,000	C

Game 20

£100	C	£200	C	£300	D
£500	A	£1,000	D	£2,000	C
£4,000	A	£8,000	C	£16,000	B
£32,000	D	£64,000	A	£125,000	D
£250,000	C	£500,000	A	£1,000,000	C

ANSWERS

Game 21

£100	D	£200	B	£300	D
£500	B	£1,000	B	£2,000	C
£4,000	B	£8,000	A	£16,000	C
£32,000	A	£64,000	C	£125,000	C
£250,000	A	£500,000	C	£1,000,000	C

Game 22

£100	D	£200	C	£300	D
£500	A	£1,000	A	£2,000	D
£4,000	C	£8,000	D	£16,000	A
£32,000	A	£64,000	D	£125,000	B
£250,000	D	£500,000	A	£1,000,000	C

Game 23

£100	D	£200	D	£300	C
£500	B	£1,000	B	£2,000	C
£4,000	C	£8,000	A	£16,000	D
£32,000	C	£64,000	A	£125,000	B
£250,000	A	£500,000	A	£1,000,000	A

Game 24

£100	B	£200	C	£300	C
£500	D	£1,000	A	£2,000	A
£4,000	B	£8,000	D	£16,000	C
£32,000	B	£64,000	A	£125,000	D
£250,000	B	£500,000	A	£1,000,000	C

Game 25

£100	D	£200	D	£300	A
£500	B	£1,000	C	£2,000	C
£4,000	B	£8,000	C	£16,000	D
£32,000	C	£64,000	A	£125,000	A
£250,000	A	£500,000	B	£1,000,000	C

Game 26

£100	B	£200	C	£300	C
£500	B	£1,000	A	£2,000	D
£4,000	B	£8,000	C	£16,000	B
£32,000	C	£64,000	D	£125,000	C
£250,000	C	£500,000	B	£1,000,000	D

Game 27

£100	D	£200	D	£300	B
£500	A	£1,000	C	£2,000	D
£4,000	B	£8,000	B	£16,000	B
£32,000	C	£64,000	D	£125,000	C
£250,000	A	£500,000	B	£1,000,000	C

Game 28

£100	C	£200	C	£300	C
£500	C	£1,000	D	£2,000	B
£4,000	D	£8,000	A	£16,000	C
£32,000	C	£64,000	A	£125,000	A
£250,000	C	£500,000	C	£1,000,000	B

Game 29

£100	B	£200	C	£300	D
£500	D	£1,000	C	£2,000	B
£4,000	C	£8,000	A	£16,000	D
£32,000	C	£64,000	D	£125,000	C
£250,000	B	£500,000	D	£1,000,000	C

Game 30

£100	C	£200	A	£300	B
£500	D	£1,000	D	£2,000	C
£4,000	D	£8,000	A	£16,000	B
£32,000	D	£64,000	B	£125,000	B
£250,000	A	£500,000	C	£1,000,000	B

ANSWERS

Game 31

£100	B	£200	B	£300	B
£500	B	£1,000	A	£2,000	B
£4,000	A	£8,000	C	£16,000	B
£32,000	A	£64,000	C	£125,000	C
£250,000	A	£500,000	D	£1,000,000	A

Game 32

£100	C	£200	A	£300	D
£500	A	£1,000	B	£2,000	A
£4,000	D	£8,000	B	£16,000	C
£32,000	A	£64,000	D	£125,000	B
£250,000	C	£500,000	A	£1,000,000	D

Game 33

£100	A	£200	C	£300	C
£500	C	£1,000	A	£2,000	A
£4,000	B	£8,000	B	£16,000	C
£32,000	D	£64,000	B	£125,000	D
£250,000	B	£500,000	A	£1,000,000	C

Game 34

£100	A	£200	B	£300	C
£500	D	£1,000	C	£2,000	B
£4,000	B	£8,000	C	£16,000	B
£32,000	D	£64,000	A	£125,000	B
£250,000	B	£500,000	B	£1,000,000	C

Game 35

£100	D	£200	D	£300	C
£500	B	£1,000	C	£2,000	A
£4,000	B	£8,000	A	£16,000	B
£32,000	B	£64,000	B	£125,000	C
£250,000	D	£500,000	D	£1,000,000	B

Game 36

£100	D	£200	C	£300	B
£500	C	£1,000	A	£2,000	D
£4,000	B	£8,000	C	£16,000	D
£32,000	D	£64,000	B	£125,000	B
£250,000	C	£500,000	C	£1,000,000	D

Game 37

£100	B	£200	B	£300	C
£500	D	£1,000	D	£2,000	A
£4,000	A	£8,000	C	£16,000	D
£32,000	A	£64,000	C	£125,000	C
£250,000	B	£500,000	A	£1,000,000	D

Game 38

£100	B	£200	C	£300	D
£500	C	£1,000	A	£2,000	B
£4,000	A	£8,000	B	£16,000	B
£32,000	B	£64,000	B	£125,000	B
£250,000	B	£500,000	D	£1,000,000	B

Game 39

£100	C	£200	B	£300	B
£500	B	£1,000	A	£2,000	B
£4,000	A	£8,000	C	£16,000	B
£32,000	C	£64,000	D	£125,000	B
£250,000	C	£500,000	C	£1,000,000	B

Game 40

£100	C	£200	B	£300	D
£500	C	£1,000	D	£2,000	A
£4,000	D	£8,000	D	£16,000	D
£32,000	D	£64,000	D	£125,000	B
£250,000	B	£500,000	B	£1,000,000	B

ANSWERS

Game 41

£100	D	£200	B	£300	B
£500	B	£1,000	C	£2,000	C
£4,000	A	£8,000	D	£16,000	B
£32,000	C	£64,000	C	£125,000	C
£250,000	B	£500,000	C	£1,000,000	C

Game 42

£100	D	£200	C	£300	D
£500	A	£1,000	D	£2,000	D
£4,000	C	£8,000	C	£16,000	A
£32,000	A	£64,000	A	£125,000	B
£250,000	C	£500,000	C	£1,000,000	C

Game 43

£100	C	£200	C	£300	D
£500	C	£1,000	A	£2,000	C
£4,000	C	£8,000	C	£16,000	C
£32,000	C	£64,000	C	£125,000	D
£250,000	B	£500,000	D	£1,000,000	C

Game 44

£100	B	£200	B	£300	A
£500	A	£1,000	C	£2,000	B
£4,000	D	£8,000	A	£16,000	A
£32,000	C	£64,000	B	£125,000	D
£250,000	B	£500,000	C	£1,000,000	A

Game 45

£100	D	£200	B	£300	B
£500	C	£1,000	A	£2,000	D
£4,000	C	£8,000	C	£16,000	A
£32,000	C	£64,000	D	£125,000	B
£250,000	C	£500,000	C	£1,000,000	A

Game 46

£100	A	£200	A	£300	C
£500	D	£1,000	B	£2,000	D
£4,000	B	£8,000	A	£16,000	A
£32,000	A	£64,000	A	£125,000	B
£250,000	C	£500,000	D	£1,000,000	C

Game 47

£100	D	£200	C	£300	D
£500	D	£1,000	A	£2,000	A
£4,000	D	£8,000	D	£16,000	D
£32,000	C	£64,000	A	£125,000	D
£250,000	B	£500,000	A	£1,000,000	A

Game 48

£100	D	£200	B	£300	C
£500	A	£1,000	B	£2,000	A
£4,000	B	£8,000	D	£16,000	C
£32,000	C	£64,000	B	£125,000	C
£250,000	C	£500,000	C	£1,000,000	C

Game 49

£100	C	£200	C	£300	B
£500	C	£1,000	D	£2,000	B
£4,000	B	£8,000	A	£16,000	A
£32,000	C	£64,000	D	£125,000	C
£250,000	A	£500,000	A	£1,000,000	C

Game 50

£100	B	£200	A	£300	B
£500	A	£1,000	C	£2,000	A
£4,000	A	£8,000	C	£16,000	C
£32,000	D	£64,000	D	£125,000	B
£250,000	B	£500,000	C	£1,000,000	C